Faith, Food & Fitness

Faith, Food & Fitness

40 DAYS TO RENEW YOUR MIND
& TRANSFORM YOUR BODY!

Charlie Jordan Brookins

FAITH, FOOD & FITNESS
Published by Purposely Created Publishing Group™

Printed in the United States of America
ISBN: 978-1-949134-29-2

For my tribe—
Greg, James Wesley, and Jordan–
I love you to the moon and back again,
and around the stars
a million trillion kabillion times.

CONTENTS

FOREWORD

Have you ever wanted a personal and practical approach to better? Better health, better habits, better skin, a better outlook and quality of life? What if learning how to become healthier was clearly outlined in an easy-to-follow, daily plan supported by God's Word? Well, ***Faith, Food & Fitness*** is your roadmap for that journey. This devotional directs you to take doable daily steps to a new you using these three powerful pillars. It doesn't matter where you are today. In 40 days, you'll be better.

Charlie Jordan Brookins wrote ***Faith, Food & Fitness*** for me, and I know she wrote it for you too! She has a unique way of communicating complex information in a profoundly simple way. Her refreshing approach to getting and staying fit—mind, body, and spirit—awakens a desire in you to be the best version of yourself.

I've known Charlie for over 20 years, and during that time I've had the opportunity to interview her for my radio show where my listeners were empowered via the airwaves. I've participated in her Fit thru Faith challenges on social media and witnessed real change in my life, on the scale and in my body.

With ***Faith, Food & Fitness***, Charlie has simplified and personalized an 8-week strategy that can last a lifetime. This devotional becomes your plan and personal trainer, powered by the Word of God. It will enable your body to better handle what work, play, delay, successes, and stresses can add to it. Whether you're learning, reinforcing, or being reminded of how to taste the Word of God daily, eat and drink food properly, or move consistently, I believe we all want to fulfill our assignments as whole and as healthy as possible.

I am absolutely convinced that Charlie has been given a gift and that she's offering it to all of us, if we'll accept it. She has become my girlfriend in whole-body health because it's her voice I hear when I make healthier choices like moving more by parking further away from an entrance. It's her smiling face I see as I prepare the "Green Leafy Goodness" smoothie she taught me how to make to start my day off right. And now, with this flavorful devotional, I have access to her words of encouragement, God's Word of instruction, and inspirational quotes to keep me motivated all day, every day! These are examples of what a good girlfriend should do, add value and see your worth.

When God divinely downloaded a burden for His people into the heart of Charlie Jordan Brookins, not one word, phrase, or concept was wasted.

She has extracted the nutrition out of every drop and blended the ingredients together meticulously. We have been afforded an opportunity to serve an entre' of excellence back to Him. They say it only takes 21 days to form a habit, so make the next 40 days of ***Faith, Food & Fitness*** the first steps to a new you!

In His Grip,
Maura Gale ~ Actress/Author/Evangelist/Host

INTRODUCTION

"My people are dying."

These four words echoed in the deepest chamber of my spirit. It was the late spring of 2006 and I had been "faith walking" for a few months, searching for direction and purpose. I was in a gray place. It wasn't dark, but it was cloudy—lacking clarity, connection, and direction. I had what many would call a "great job" in the entertainment industry, but the creative environment was becoming increasingly corporate. Morale was low and I just wasn't settled in my spirit. I had also been married for just under two years, and our efforts to conceive weren't bearing fruit. I felt depleted and disconnected.

I recalled a book that I had read several years prior entitled *Experiencing God* by Henry & Richard Blackaby, and Claude Knight—a highly recommended read! There are seven principles outlined in the book for seeking the will of God. All seven principles are on point, but the two that stuck like glue were the first and third:

> Principle #1 – *God is always at work around you.*
>
> Principle #3 – *God invites you to become involved with Him in His work.*

My remixed version is: *"Seek where God is at work and join Him."*

And that's just what I did. I started a practice of "faith walking," a practice I still enjoy today. Every morning, ear buds out, I walked with an intention and purpose to hear a word of direction and instruction. Candidly, there were days of "crickets" and static, but then one day the Holy Spirit spoke the words that would change the course of my life. "*My people are dying.*" My feet stopped dead in their tracks as I asked for clarification, "Come again?"

"My people are dying" was the response. I'm not one who has an open chat-line with the Most High, so this was a moment. It used to bug me when my friends or husband would say, "The Holy Spirit told me..." to do this or that, because I thought there might be too much static on my line. But these words were clear, and they resonated like a bell. I certainly knew of the growing pandemic of obesity and preventable diseases like Type 2 diabetes, stroke, and heart disease that were taking the lives of those I loved and admired far too soon.

My uncle, who was an ordained minister and medical doctor, prided himself on knowing a little something about everything, yet he dropped dead of a heart attack at the age of 54. He knew a little about a lot, but not about the importance of eating more veggies and moving daily to release the dangerous hard fat around his belly. My grandmother never fully recovered from burying her baby boy.

Those haunting words were clear, but something wasn't quite right. The bible says in John 10:10 (NKJ), "*I have come that they may have life, and that they may have it more abundantly.*" Now, my brain thinks pretty logically. If Jesus came to give us an abundant life and "*my people were dying,*" then "my people" were missing something critical. Clearly there was a disconnect somewhere.

I did more searching and seeking (and walking) to understand the missing link, as well as my role. Day after day, step after step, the vision for Fit thru Faith came raining down so I could write it down and make it plain for you.

During that time, I questioned God at every turn. "Are you sure this is what you want me to do?" "Why me?" Despite my questioning, the vision kept flowing, so I stopped questioning and started obeying. Imagine that.

Of course there were distractions—life, getting pregnant twice, my F.U.D. (fear, uncertainty, and doubt) and job distractions. After a successful launch of the first Fit thru Faith program at my church, I was blessed with a gift-wrapped opportunity in the television industry. The creative and corporate job demands prevented me from sowing into Fit thru Faith for seven years. In the eighth year (the number of new beginnings), I was obedient and transitioned to serve on this mission field full-time.

I share this story because it's important for you to know who you are partnering with on this 40-day adventure. As a certified health coach and personal fitness trainer, I have the education, expertise, and results to support your health and fitness goals. But what yo u really need to know is that it's my call and my purpose to be a bridge to your breakthrough in your whole-body health.

It's also important for you to know that I'm not a genetically slender person. "Chunky" was actually the word my grandmother used to describe me as an adolescent. I know the waistline challenges that my grandmothers, mother, and sister have battled. I've ridden the roller coaster of emotional eating and weight change after heartbreak, career uncertainty, multiple hip surgeries and giving birth to two children naturally in my 40's. I've worn out the "no time" excuse for not prioritizing my health due to a hectic work and travel schedule, church commitments, and home life with a husband and young children. I've faced the mirror with my menopausal middle, believing that it was something that I just needed to biologically accept. Don't believe the hype!

I have not walked in your shoes, but I am shades of your story. I wake up each morning in my "service size body" because I do the work. I show up for myself, those I love and who love me, and for the purpose and call that God has on my life. I made a decision to be non-negotiable about my faith, food, and fitness—not just for my future, but to look, feel and serve my best today. I made a choice not to wait for an event or a doctor's threats to force a change. I made a choice to live fully NOW, and you can too.

There are still days when my choices are not the healthiest, but I am mindful about making a healthier choice the next day. What about you? Are you lacking energy, frustrated with brain fog, achy joints, or more weight than your body was built for? Are you standing on a conveyor belt that's destined for medication, fatigue, and dependence on others? Well, it's not too late to jump off to reclaim your energy and ignite your purpose. It's not too late to look and feel better now and live out your "*latter shall be greater*" years (Haggai 2:9) with more joy and vitality. The victory is already yours, so suit up in your full armor (Ephesians 6:11-18) and set your course for success in these next 40 days.

YOUR 40-DAY ADVENTURE

Before I unpack your 40-day adventure, let me just love on you a little. There's a praise party going on in your honor at this moment. Your decision to read this book is absolutely worth some virtual confetti! Transforming your whole-body health is not easy but it is doable, and you've taken the first action step.

Commitment + Consistency = CHANGE. This book gives you the unique opportunity to honor your commitments with consistent action, one day at a time for **40 days!** You have a bold, beautiful, God-given gift to share with this world and you need your best health to support that call. So, let's do this!

For clarity, this is not a "get thin quick" manual. Instead, this devotional shares small, actionable **faith, food and fitness** steps to support and empower a new you. **Faith** is your foundation. **Food** is your fuel. **Fitness** is your battery.

FAITH IS YOUR FOUNDATION

"Unless the Lord builds the house,
the builders labor in vain."
—Psalms 127:1 (NIV)

If you've been wondering why statistics state over 90 percent of the diets you've tried have failed long term, look no further than this verse. Diets are based on some form of deprivation and willpower, which is limited and unsustainable. When you live Fit thru Faith, you are fueled by abundant and unlimited spirit power. And "*where the spirit of the Lord is, there is freedom*" (2 Corinthians 3:17 KJV). You'll find freedom from the behaviors and thoughts that have kept you stuck in your stuff and avoiding the mirror. And here's a secret—it's been with you all the time.

Your adventure begins by plugging into your power source and truly believing that you have a unique God-given seed of purpose to make your epic impact on this world! And when I say epic, I mean "*exceedingly abundantly above all that you ask or think*" epic (Ephesians 2:21 NKJ).

FOOD IS YOUR FUEL

The next step is making a mindset shift from eating food to **nourishing your temple.**

"Do you not know that your ***bodies are temples*** *of the Holy Spirit,*
who is in you, whom you have received from God?
You are not your own;
you were bought at a price. Therefore honor God with your bodies."

—1 Corinthians 6:19-20 (NIV)

It's time to start honoring the gift that God has given you by getting into connection with what you put into your temple. As Dr. Mark Hyman says, "*Food is information.*" What you eat directs a physiological response in your body. When you eat healthy single ingredient foods from God's abundant buffet, your body knows what to do with it. It knows how to use those yummy raw materials to nourish and energize your body. On the other hand, when you eat predominantly man-made, lab-created foods that are foreign to your body and your vocabulary, the response is excess fat storage and inflammation, which is the seed of disease.

And what exactly should you be eating? Well, what does the Bible say?

"Then God said, "I give you every seed-bearing plant on the face of the whole earth and every tree that has fruit with seed in it. They will be yours for food."

—Genesis 1:29 (NIV)

The first mention of food in the Bible is very clear. **Plant-based foods should be your foundation.** These are the first foods. These are the foods that God created for you to survive and thrive, which is why it's not surprising that they give you the most health, healing, and life. And despite the confusion and conflicting approaches of many popular and reputable dietary theories out there, this is an area where there's pretty much universal agreement. Why? Because God said it, and He is "*not the author of confusion*" (1 Corinthians 14:33 KJV).

I've made a personal choice to be plant-exclusive (vegan), but that's not what I'm talking about here. What I'm talking about is being plant-powered by "crowding in" more healthy and healing plant-based foods to fill your plate. When you "crowd in" the God-made goodness, you organically "crowd out" the man-made stuff that is showing up around your middle. The mantra is—**"If God made it, eat it. If man made it, reduce it!"**

FITNESS IS YOUR BATTERY

"Faith by itself, if it is not accompanied by action, is dead."

—James 2:17 (NIV)

You can't will yourself fit. You can't believe yourself fit. You have to get into action. The generally recognized physical activity guidelines from many health agencies is consistent:

Overall:

- Be active! Any activity is better than none.

Aerobic Activity:

- 150 minutes (approx. 30 minutes for 5 days) each week of moderate-intensity aerobic activity (Ex. brisk walking)
- OR 75 minutes each week of vigorous-intensity aerobic activity (Ex. jogging, swimming laps, high intensity interval training (HIIT)
- Aim for a minimum of 10 minutes for each session. Multiple sessions throughout the day do add up. (Ex. A 10-minute "faith walk" in the AM + a 10-minute power walk with co-workers at lunch + a 10-minute de-stress brisk walk after work = 30 minutes!)

The guidelines above are focused on health rather than weight release. If weight release is your goal, you'll want to consider increasing, even doubling, the numbers above. But don't let anything stop you from getting started. Begin with just 5–10 minutes a day with an activity that you enjoy and **be consistent**. Pick a time when you're least likely to get distracted and put it in your calendar. I repeat—put it in your calendar. Once you develop a consistent practice with 5–10 minutes each day, add 5 minutes. You'll start to feel so good that you'll make more time.

Strength:

- 2 or more sessions per week of moderate or high intensity strength moves involving all major muscle groups (think weights, resistance bands, kettle balls, even body weight).

  I can't overemphasize how important it is for you to do some form of consistent strength training. It's not about bodybuilding, it's about life building. As you age gracefully, you are losing muscle mass and bone density. As you lose muscle mass, your metabolism slows and your belly grows. But you can actively do something about it. Two to three 20-30 minute sessions per week go a long way to a sexier silhouette and a healthier and happier body.

Here's the bottom-line: When your fitness battery is charged up daily, you have more power mentally and physically to do all that God has called you to do. Conversely, when your fitness battery has little to no charge, your body and your mind slow down. It's as simple as that. Physical fitness is about making daily deposits, which can vary in length and scope—and it's never too late to start, whether you're 18 or 80. If time is an issue, don't let that be your excuse to do nothing.

Let's put it all together. When your **faith, food and fitness** are interconnected and firing at a high level, your life becomes lighter and brighter. The excess weight melts away without you even focusing on it. The result is more energy, creativity, and confidence to live boldly in what I call your "service size body"—to be of greatest service to God and the world.

So why 40 days? The number 40 is very popular in the Bible, and is normally associated with periods of trial, test, and transition. For example:

- In the story of Noah and the Ark, it rained for **40 days**
- Moses and the Israelites wandered in the wilderness of Egypt for **40 years**
- Moses was on Mt. Sinai for **40 days** before returning with the stone tablets
- Jesus was tempted by the devil after **40 days** of fasting
- Jesus appeared for **40 days** after His resurrection

I challenge you to consecrate these next 40 days as a test and trial period to renew your mind and transform your body into a healthier version of you. This is a great opportunity for you to ignite your belief system, commit to yourself, complete what you say you're going to do, and celebrate your success!

I couldn't be more excited to share this message of ***Faith, Food & Fitness*** with you through this 40-day devotional. Over the years, by God's grace, I have witnessed testimony after testimony of what happens when you plug into your power source to replace willpower with spiritual power, replace "man's food" with God's food, and replace a sedentary lifestyle with stability, stamina, and strength-building action.

This devotional is only the beginning. Your journey to whole-body health is a marathon. Each day you must be intentional about your commitment to better health. This is not about a fruitless pursuit of perfection, but instead a daily pursuit of progress and "God's better" on the road to God's best. It's about loving yourself as God does and owning your worth.

My prayer is that the meditations, inspiration, motivation, and action steps in this devotional will take deep root in your spirit and ignite a new season of transformational change in your life.

HOW TO USE THIS BOOK

First, if you haven't read the introduction, I highly recommend that you go back and take a quick read. You won't regret it. This book is set up to be explored in 8 weeks, but you can certainly stretch it out to suit your needs and mix up the weeks as you desire. There are 40 Bible-based mantras and 8 weekly challenges. I encourage you to meditate on the mantras and scripture throughout the day, and explore your reflections in writing as you wind down at night. Whether it is one word, one sentence, or an entire page, get your thoughts out of your head and into written form. If you get stuck, consider writing it out as a prayer. Ask for clarity and guidance with challenge areas and celebrate your wins—aka M.O.P.s (Moments of Praise). On the weekends, I encourage you to review the weekly mantras and continue with the challenges to reinforce your new habits.

On this ***Faith, Food & Fitness*** journey, you will be building an adventure toolkit of tips and tools to support your action steps. Think of it like a passport to prepare you for your next stop. You will also find additional resources and bonus downloads on the website: **www.fitthrufaith.com.**

Achieving better health is absolutely possible when you connect your faith and food with your whole-body fitness, making small powerful changes one day at a time. You can truly do "*all things through Christ who strengthens you*" (Philippians 4:13 NKJV). Enjoy the adventure!

BEFORE YOU GET STARTED

I know you're anxious to get started, but DON'T SKIP this section! Before you launch out into the deep, it's critical that you have a compass to help navigate the inevitable choppy waters.

Your compass is your **Big Bold Why** (BBW). Setting out on an adventure without a purpose and intention is setting yourself up for failure. Why **must** you have better health right now? Who is depending on you? What purpose and call are on your life? And if you don't know, get to seeking. You were "*created to do good works*" (Ephesians 2:10 NIV), and the world needs more of you.

The key words are **Big** and **Bold**. Wearing *this* dress for *that* reunion isn't going to get you a lifetime lifestyle change. Short term goals = short term results! But a **Big Bold Why** will go the distance!

My BBW has a few elements to it. One is being able to move the same way, and with the same mental clarity and energy, for my future grandchildren as I do for my kids today. It's very likely that I will be in my 80's when my grandchildren are my kids' current ages, and I want to be fly, spry, and medication free. The thought of needing to depend on my children when they are in the prime of their lives is enough to get my behind up in the morning to move.

The other element of my BBW is you. I have to walk my talk in order to be a sturdy bridge to a healthier version of you. The beauty is that as I prioritize and pour into my health for the future, I get the immediate benefits of looking, feeling, and serving bigger and better today. Now it's your turn. Here are a few BBW ground rules:

#1: **Your BBW needs to be bigger than you.** Why? Because you're likely to let yourself down, so focus on **service**. One of my clients in the healthcare field wasn't walking her talk. Being a role model and health ambassador on the job became her BBW. Another client wanted to get off of her blood pressure medication to be more active and present for her grandchildren.

#2: **Your BBW should have a long-term focus**. Otherwise, it's simply a goal. Getting off blood pressure medication is an awesome goal—and I highly recommend you talk to your doctor about how you can do just that—but then what? Getting off medication should fuel your Big Bold Why. But your actual BBW is even bigger than that. What is your passion? How can you be of greater service once you have a body and life you love?

#3: **Your BBW should be white hot.** It should excite you. It's the reason you don't hit the snooze button, and why you go to a farmer's market for local produce, cook more, get the sleep you need, and practice more self-care.

Take a stab at it. It may change over the course of these 40 days, but it should fuel and inspire you daily to do more and be more. Pray about it and listen.

My **Big Bold Why** is....

____

____

____

____

____

____

____

____

If you need a little more inspiration, choose a **theme song** for these 40 days. Play it each morning to get the party started each day.

My theme song is:

____

____

Now that you're clear on your Big Bold Why, let's set your intention.

STEP ONE: Strong Start—Strong Finish!

How do you want to feel at the beginning and end of your 40 days?

Example:

At the **beginning** of the 40 days, I want to feel optimistic and open.
At the **end** of the 40 days, I want to feel committed to my whole-body health.

At the beginning of the 40 days, I want to feel...

____

____

At the end of the 40 days, I want to feel...

____

____

STEP TWO: Hopes & Dreams

What are three specific reasons you are embarking on this adventure?

Example:

I want to release my self-sabotaging thoughts regarding my body.

I want to grow closer to God.

I want to have more energy.

____

____

____

____

____

____

STEP THREE: Be Intentional!

Use the sentiments in the previous questions to write out your intention for your 40-day adventure.

What is your intention for the next 40 days?

Example:

My intention for these 40 days is to show up optimistic and open. Each day, I intend to release my self-sabotaging thoughts, grow closer to God, and have more energy. By the end of these 40 days, I intend to be committed to my whole-body health.

____

____

____

____

____

____

____

____

____

Let's go!

WEEK #1
HYDRATION CHALLENGE

"Every morning I look fear, overwhelm, and doubt in the face and tell them, 'Not today! My God is bigger!'"

Welcome to week one! You know that God hasn't given you a "*spirit of fear*" (2 Timothy 1:7), but the emotion of fear is real. You have a choice to let that feeling fuel you rather than paralyze you on this journey. When my kids say they're scared, I tell them, "That's awesome! I'm excited, too. God must be about to do something big!" You are doing a new thing, so trust and believe that obstacles will try to get in the way. The negative chatter and voices are going to pump up the volume. Each morning this week, stare them down in the mirror and tell them, **"Not today! My God is bigger!"** Happy launching!

ADVENTURE TOOLKIT

(Visit www.fitthrufaith.com for additional Week #1 resources and support)

Optional Shopping List:

- Portable Water Bottle (metal or glass preferred)
- Your Favorite Spa Water Infusers (i.e. Cucumber, Strawberries, Lemons, Oranges, etc.)
- Your Favorite Green or Herbal Tea

WEEK #1 – DAY #1

AFFIRMATION: ***I am a Doer!***

FOUNDATION/MEDITATION: "But be **doers** of the word, and not hearers only, deceiving yourselves." *—James 1:22 (NKJV)*

"In the same way, faith by itself, if it is not accompanied by action, is dead." *—James 2:17 (NIV)*

INSPIRATION: "Do or do not—there is no try!" *—Yoda*

MOTIVATION: You are a Doer. It's time to stop talking about it and start being about it. **Action** is the antidote to just about everything including fear. It's time to take captive any thoughts, behaviors and influences that have been keeping you from your "service size body" and get into action. What small action step can you take today to have the biggest impact on your whole-body health?

PRAYER STARTER: *Thank you for your Word. Help me to be a doer and not just a hearer. I am committed to doing a new thing in my whole-body health. Help me stay consistent one day at a time. In Jesus' Name, Amen.*

ACTION: Hydration Week – Day #1

Your first challenge week is all about H2O! Your body is approximately 60 percent water. You can't survive more than 3 days without it. Drinking water is also linked to weight release and overall health, so drink up! Your goal this week is to not only drink more water, but to replace some of those sugary drinks like soda (regular and diet—yes, I'm going there!), sweet tea, sugary coffee drinks, fruit juice, etc. with God's most refreshing drink.

TODAY: Make water your first meal of the day. Squeeze the juice of a lemon half to jumpstart your body and your day. Drink **at least 8 ounces** of water before each meal or snack. Keep your favorite water bottle nearby to sip throughout the day. Don't start eating before you get your water in first. Not only will you hydrate your body, but you'll also start to fill you up. **48 oz.** is your minimum today, but if you're already there, your goal is to **drink more** and ultimately target half of your body weight in ounces of water.

REFLECTIONS:

WEEK #1 – DAY #2

AFFIRMATION: *I am a Partaker of His Promise!*

FOUNDATION/MEDITATION: "That the Gentiles should be fellow heirs, and of the same body, and the **partakers of his promise** in Christ by the gospel." —*Ephesians 3:6 (KJV)*

"For I know the plans I have for you," declares the Lord, "plans to prosper you and not to harm you, plans to give you hope and a future." —*Jeremiah 29:11 (NIV)*

INSPIRATION: "God never made a promise that was too good to be true." —*Dwight L. Moody*

MOTIVATION: The promises of God are far too many to list. If you want to be overwhelmed by just how much God loves you, just Google "Promises of God" and take them all in. One truth you can cling to each day is that you have a purpose, a hope, and a future. When you take care of your temple, you are in the best position to fulfill and receive all that God has promised.

PRAYER STARTER: *Thank you for your promises. They are too numerous to list. Help me to live in purpose, on purpose today as I strive to take better care of my temple. In Jesus' Name, Amen.*

ACTION: Hydration Week – Day #2
Drinking water helps increase your energy and flush out those pesky toxins that build up daily from the food we eat, the products we use and the environment around us. When your body is toxic with chronic inflammation from overindulging in fast, packaged and processed foods, it doesn't function at its best—and who wants that? When your body is properly hydrated, you not only feel better, but you perform better.

TODAY: How's the morning lemon water going? Fresh squeezed is always best, but if you're struggling to get it in, you can grab the organic squeezed lemon juice in a bottle. Drink **at least 8 ounces** of water before each meal or snack, and continue to sip from your favorite water bottle throughout the day when you're thirsty. If you're a busy multi-tasker like me and forget to drink, try sipping for a count of 10 before putting your bottle or glass down to get more bang for each sip. Be patient with yourself. You are developing a new habit and it will take time. We'll take it up a notch tomorrow. The daily minimum is **48 oz**. for one more day, but feel free to beat it.

REFLECTIONS:

WEEK #1 – DAY #3

AFFIRMATION: *I am a Temple!*

FOUNDATION/MEDITATION: "Do you not know that your bodies are **temples of the Holy Spirit**, who is in you, whom you have received from God? You are not your own; you were bought at a price. Therefore, honor God with your bodies." *—1 Corinthians 6:19-20 (NIV)*

INSPIRATION: "Take care of your body. It's the only place you have to live." *—Jim Rohn*

MOTIVATION: Taking responsibility for the gift that God has loaned to you is one of the first steps of living your "divinely designed healthy lifestyle." The next step is taking care of your temple by feeding it the yummy food that God created, and consistently moving your body. It's time to make a mindset shift from eating food to nourishing your temple. Be mindful of the food on your plate today—really see it. Is it filled with nourishing goodness from God's abundant buffet? These are the foods that will "do your temple good."

PRAYER STARTER: *Thank you for gifting me with my body. It is your temple. Help me to nourish and fuel my temple with the foods that you created for me to survive and thrive. In Jesus' Name, Amen.*

ACTION: Hydration Week – Day #3
Water makes you look good and feel good by supporting your immune system. As you age gracefully, skincare creeps up on the priority list, so enjoy every last drop of water today. Continue to aim for 10 gulps before you put your glass or bottle down.

TODAY: Try spa water! Add slices of cucumber, strawberries and/or citrus fruit to your water, and increase your intake to **12 ounces** before each meal and sip throughout the day. We're moving our daily goal up to **56 ounces today**. You've got this!

REFLECTIONS:

WEEK #1 – DAY #4

AFFIRMATION: *I am A Treasured Possession!*

FOUNDATION/MEDITATION: "For you are a people holy to the Lord your God. The Lord your God has chosen you out of all the peoples on the face of the earth to be his people, **his treasured possession**." *—Deuteronomy 7:6 (NIV)*

INSPIRATION: "The best way to keep your spirits up? Never forget the treasure that you are." *—Unknown*

MOTIVATION: Sometimes you need to be reminded just how amazing you are. You are treasured and dearly loved—not perfect, but "flawsome." Even with your beautiful imperfections, you are still God's treasure. He loves you just the way you are, the way He crafted you. As a reminder, make a list of at least **5 attributes** that make you "flawsome" in the "Reflections" section for today. **Don't skip this exercise**! And you don't have to limit yourself to 5. Write down at least 5 and own them all day long!

PRAYER STARTER: *Thank you for loving me as your treasured possession. I know I am precious in your sight. Help me to see and value myself in the same way. In Jesus' Name, Amen.*

ACTION: Hydration Week – Day #4
Another great benefit of water is that it helps your body's flow (aka keeping you regular). To keep things moving, stay hydrated and enjoy water and fiber-rich foods like cucumbers, dark green leafy and cruciferous veggies, or citrus fruits like oranges and apples. Get the most bang for your buck with a power pack combo of antioxidants, fiber, and water.

TODAY: If you're starting to get bored, swap in an occasional green or herbal tea (hot or iced) to get your **12 ounces** of water before each meal. Start to inch towards half of your body weight in ounces for the entire day, but at least **64 oz.**

REFLECTIONS:

WEEK #1 – DAY #5

AFFIRMATION: ***I am Accepted!***

FOUNDATION/MEDITATION: "Accept one another, then, just as **Christ accepted you**, in order to bring praise to God." *—Romans 15:7 (NIV)*

INSPIRATION: "Be yourself, because the people who mind don't matter, and the people who matter don't mind." *—Dr. Seuss*

MOTIVATION: One of my favorite Billy Joel songs is "I Love You Just the Way You Are." It should come as no surprise that the God who crafted you in His image also loves and accepts you just the way you are. But have you accepted yourself? You may be disappointed with the reflection in the mirror, but God sees beyond your image into your possibility. Begin to see yourself through His loving and accepting eyes each time you look in the mirror.

PRAYER STARTER: *Thank you for accepting me, flaws and all. Help me to accept myself and to make food and fitness choices that honor my temple and give you glory. In Jesus' Name, Amen.*

ACTION: Hydration Week – Day #5
You've reached Day #5 of the water challenge! Now just keep it up into the weekend and beyond. Remind yourself of the success strategies you used during the week. What are your biggest obstacles to consistently drink more water? What strategies can you use to overcome them? Jot them down in the "Reflections" section. Keep up the great work!

TODAY: Let's stretch to **12–16 ounces** before/ during each meal as you close in on half of your body weight in ounces for the day. Don't guzzle. Intentionally sip throughout the day. And how about a new stylish aluminum or glass water bottle in your favorite color to celebrate and remind yourself of the importance of this new practice?

REFLECTIONS:

WEEK #2 – GET TO STEPPIN' CHALLENGE

"You're never going to feel like it."

Week #2 is here! If the water challenge wasn't your jam, stay the course. There's a new challenge this week, as well as more time to keep working that water in, slowly, but surely.

Now it's time to get real. If you're not working out regularly or eating as healthy as you know you need to, it's not likely that you're going to **feel** like doing it. Living in better whole-body health is not a feeling, it's a **doing**! "Assume the position" of a healthier person. "Act as if" you were in better health. What does that look like for you? The more you show up for yourself, the better you will feel. And the better you feel, the more you will actually feel like doing the thing that makes you feel good. Make sense? Nike got it right. Just do it!

ADVENTURE TOOLKIT

(Visit www.fitthrufaith.com for additional Week #2 resources and support)

- Step Tracker (wearable or step tracking app download)

WEEK #2 – DAY #6

AFFIRMATION: ***I am an Overcomer!***

FOUNDATION/MEDITATION: "You, dear children, are from God and **have overcome them**, because the one who is in you is greater than the one who is in the world." *—1 John 4:4 (NIV)*

INSPIRATION: "When you begin to accept the fact that your true identity includes being an overcomer, you will never settle for less than a miracle." *—Craig Groeschel*

MOTIVATION: You are an overcomer. You've been through some things—some things that are hard to mention without being overwhelmed by the goodness of God. Write a few of those milestones down. What have you and God accomplished together? And more importantly, what was your success strategy? Take a moment to acknowledge and write down what makes you successful in other areas of your life. How can you use these same strategies and tools in your whole-body health practice? Overcoming is in your DNA, so apply that power to make small but impactful changes in your health and life.

PRAYER STARTER: *Thank you for reminding me that I am an overcomer. I am ready for whatever this day has to bring. There is nothing that we can't handle and overcome together. In Jesus' Name, Amen.*

ACTION: Get to Steppin' Challenge – Day #1

Now that you're hydrated, it's time to move. This week's challenge focuses on being a "power player." A power player looks for every opportunity to be in action. A great way to be intentional and connected with your physical activity is to **track your steps.** This practice also adds a layer of accountability. As Maya Angelou said, "*When you know better, you do better.*"

TODAY: It's time to find the box, dust it off and put your wearable step tracker on your wrist. And if you don't have one, you can download a free app for your phone and use a fanny pack to keep your phone close by. Today's goal is **5,000–7,500 steps**. If you're already hitting that mark on the regular, set a goal to challenge yourself. Write it down and slay the day!

REFLECTIONS:

WEEK #2 – DAY #7

AFFIRMATION: ***I am Blameless!***

FOUNDATION/MEDITATION: "Yet now he has reconciled you to himself through the death of Christ in his physical body. As a result, he has brought you into his own presence, and you are holy and **blameless** as you stand before him without a single fault." *—Colossians 1:22 (NLT)*

INSPIRATION: "Yesterday is history, tomorrow is a mystery, today is a gift of God, which is why we call it the present." *—Bil Keane*

MOTIVATION: Being blameless doesn't mean that you never do anything wrong, but it does mean that you have nothing to hide in God's presence. There's no shame in your game. I don't believe in "cheat days," only "choice days." As an adult with free will, you should be able to choose an indulgent treat without guilt or the feeling that you are "cheating" or doing something wrong. But it's also important to get up the next day and **make the choice** to drink more water, eat more veggies, and take that walk you've been putting off. Take responsibility for your health and do everything in the light without blame or shame.

PRAYER STARTER: Thank you for your grace and mercy. Help me to live a life that is blameless before you. Help me to take ownership and make food choices in the light without guilt or shame. In Jesus' Name, Amen.

ACTION: Get to Steppin' Challenge – Day #2
When you move, you remind your muscles, joints and heart to continue to support God's call on your life. You need them to work for you, so show them some love and attention. You can also reduce the risk, prevent and even correct chronic diseases like heart disease, high blood pressure, obesity and Type 2 diabetes. It's a win-win!

TODAY: Today, the goal is **5,500–8,000 steps**. If you didn't reach your goal yesterday, what was the obstacle? How can you overcome that obstacle today?

REFLECTIONS:

WEEK #2 – DAY #8

AFFIRMATION: ***I am Blessed!***

FOUNDATION/MEDITATION: "I will make you into a great nation, and I will **bless** you; I will make your name great, and you will be a blessing."
—Genesis 12:2 (NIV)

"And God is able to **bless you abundantly**, so that in all things at all times, having all that you need, you will abound in every good work."
—2 Corinthians 1:8 (NIV)

INSPIRATION: "Blessed are those who give without remembering and receive without forgetting."
—Elizabeth Bibesco

MOTIVATION: Not only are you blessed, but you're a blessing to others. This is where you really shine. But in order to give your best to God and others, you need to first invest time and energy in yourself. Self-care needs to be non-negotiable. Taking small moments to recharge and renew is not a selfish act, it's a loving act that supports your purpose and your whole-body health. If time wasn't an issue, what's the first thing that you would do for yourself? How would you feel? Now make a plan to get a slice of that feeling for the rest of the week. What is realistic? Even if it's 5 minutes a day—what can you do? Quiet time? Meditation? Dance party? Moving daily and nourishing your body with whole, clean, nutrient dense foods supports your passion to serve others and the world.

PRAYER STARTER: *Thank you for blessing me. Help me to be a blessing to others today. Help me see where you are at work, so I can join you. In Jesus' Name, Amen.*

ACTION: Get to Steppin' Challenge – Day #3

Sweat sessions are important for heart, brain and overall health. But you also have an opportunity to burn more calories throughout the day without sweating out your hair during the "in between" time. Park and walk instead of looking for the closest parking space. Take the stairs when possible. Take a 10-30 minute stroll at lunch. Get a standing desk and march in place while you're typing those long emails. Look for every opportunity to move!

TODAY: Today your goal is **6,000–8,500 steps**. What worked for you yesterday? Do it again. What didn't work? Try something new. Stretch for the number that challenges you.

REFLECTIONS:

WEEK #2 – DAY #9

AFFIRMATION: ***I am Bold!***

FOUNDATION/MEDITATION: "The wicked flee though no one pursues, but the righteous are as **bold as a lion**." *—Proverbs 28:1 (NIV)*

INSPIRATION: "Freedom lies in being bold." – *Robert Frost*

MOTIVATION: Not only are you bold, but you also have a bold and beautiful gift to share with this world. Shut down the negative chatter, the fear, and the "hateration" and share your gift and message with boldness. When the voices in your head are not saying nice things to you—news flash! – that's not God! What is God telling you to do that you have yet to move on? Take one bold step today!

PRAYER STARTER: *Thank you for your boldness. Help me to boldly move forward in my purpose and possibility today. In Jesus' Name, Amen.*

ACTION: Get to Steppin' Challenge – Day #4
When you're in action, you feel better. Stress, fear, and anxiety fade because you are fully alive and present in your body. I love "faith walking" first thing in the morning. When I'm intentional and listening, I get direction and clarity. My creativity also fires on all cylinders when I take the time to get away from my work and home environment and seek Him first. If you usually listen to music when you walk, try walking without the ear buds today and seek what you need as you move.

TODAY: Today, let's take the goal up to **7,000–9,500 steps**. Schedule time when you are least likely to be distracted and get it done!

REFLECTIONS:

WEEK #2 – DAY #10

AFFIRMATION: ***I am Chosen!***

FOUNDATION/MEDITATION: "Therefore, as **God's chosen people**, holy and dearly loved, clothe yourselves with compassion, kindness, humility, gentleness, and patience." —*Colossians 3:12 (NIV)*

"You did not choose me, **but I chose you** and appointed you so that you might go and bear fruit..." —*John 15:16 (NIV)*

INSPIRATION: "Life isn't about finding yourself, it is about discovering who God created you to be." —*Unknown*

MOTIVATION: You can't be reminded enough how special you are. Why? Because you're not going to do it. Sadly, you spend too much time pointing out all of your "flaws" and the things you haven't accomplished. God wants to remind you that you are chosen and created with a purpose. God made a choice to bring you into this world. What choices are you going to make to manifest your special message in this world?

PRAYER STARTER: *Thank you for choosing me. Help me to see my value and manifest your message in this world. In Jesus' Name, Amen.*

ACTION: Get to Steppin' Challenge – Day #5

Have you heard the phrase, "sitting is the new smoking"? Well, sadly the research supports the statement. Some reports state that you shouldn't sit for more than 30 minutes without getting up to stretch and move for at least 3 minutes. Set an alarm and stay in action. If 30 minutes isn't possible, move 5–10 minutes every hour. If an hour isn't doable, move 10–20 minutes every two hours. The quality and quantity of your life depends on it.

TODAY: Today's goal is **7,500–10,000 steps**. This week's challenge may be over, but the lifestyle habit of daily activity should continue into this weekend and beyond. Reinforce the actions you're taking that are working by being consistent.

REFLECTIONS:

WEEK #3 – RADICAL LABEL READING CHALLENGE

"The healthiest foods in the market are the quietest."

—Michael Pollan

You made it to Week 3! Celebrate that! You may already know the healthy tip to "shop the perimeter" of the grocery store where you'll find your produce, protein and more of the single ingredient foods from God's abundant buffet. But I love the quote above as a guide for when you venture into the deep of the aisles. Beware of "noisy labels." Packages that have a lot of health claims on the front are often hiding some sneaky chemicals and fillers on the back. Don't be duped by the large colorful print! Read the small print on the label. If you don't know what it is or how to pronounce it, your body doesn't either. The Big Food industry spends millions of dollars in marketing and on lab-created chemicals and flavors to keep you coming back for foods that are not kind to your body. God-made food doesn't have to boast because it's 100 percent real—no labels needed. Learn to love the foods that love you back.

ADVENTURE TOOLKIT

(Visit www.fitthrufaith.com for Week #3 resources and support)

WEEK #3 – DAY #11

AFFIRMATION: *I am Comforted!*

FOUNDATION/MEDITATION: "Even though I walk through the darkest valley, I will fear no evil, for you are with me; your rod and your staff, they **comfort me**." —*Psalms 23:4 (NIV)*

INSPIRATION: "Come to me all you who are weary and burdened, and I will give you rest." —*Matthew 11:28 (NIV)*

MOTIVATION: We all go through seasons in our lives—seasons of joy, seasons of sorrow, seasons of success, seasons of challenge, and endless seasons of busyness. God sees it all. He knows which season is coming before you do. But He also doesn't give you more than you can bear, and always makes a way for you (Isaiah 43:16). He will comfort you when stress knocks at your door. When you start to reach for those Oreos or potato chips and aren't even hungry, seek His comfort. If hunger isn't the problem, Oreos aren't the solution. Check in with yourself to get to the root of what you're really feeling. Begin to unpack what's at the heart of your "need to feed." Seek Him first!

PRAYER STARTER: *Thank you for your comfort and your peace. Help me get to the root of my eating choices today. In Jesus' Name, Amen.*

ACTION: Radical Label Reading Challenge – Day #1

This week it's time for you to become a **radical label reader (RLR).** A radical label reader doesn't put anything into their body until they know everything that's in it. It's as simple as that. You wouldn't let a stranger into your house, yet you invite strange food and chemicals into your body every day. This week you will begin building the practice of reading labels consistently. Your goal is to get into connection with what you're putting into your body. Remember the mantra—**"If God made it, eat it. If man made it, reduce it!"**

TODAY: Let's start your RLR adventure in your house. Explore the labels on the packaged goods and cans in your cabinets, refrigerator and freezer. How many ingredients are God-made vs. "man-made"? How many ingredients are foreign words you can't pronounce? Google a few of the repetitive words. What are the pros and cons of the lab-created ingredients? How can you make a better choice the next time you go to the grocery store?

REFLECTIONS:

WEEK #3 – DAY #12

AFFIRMATION: ***I am Complete!***

FOUNDATION/MEDITATION: "For in Him dwells all the fullness of the Godhead bodily; and **you are complete** in Him, who is the head of all principality and power." *—Colossians 2:9-10 (NKJV)*

INSPIRATION: "You don't need someone to complete you. You only need someone to accept you completely." *—Unknown*

MOTIVATION: You are complete. You have everything you need to do and be everything that God has purposed. You are enough—strong enough, smart enough, bold enough—all that! God has given you the complete owner's manual (aka the Bible) to move boldly in your call. If you're not living or striving to "enjoy good health" (3 John 1:2 NIV), you're leaving money on the table, short changing your dreams, and stunting your service to this world. You know what you need to do. Your spiritual toolkit is stocked. Make a consistent commitment to be a better you—one day at a time.

PRAYER STARTER: *Thank you for your Word. Thank you for your seed of purpose. Help me to water that seed today with healthy food choices. In Jesus' Name, Amen.*

ACTION: Radical Label Reading Challenge – Day #2

One of the first things that can derail your radical label reading journey is the **serving size**, which is easy to find at the top of your label. It's important to identify this number because your idea of a serving may be different than the actual serving size of the product. For example, if a serving of potato chips for you is a whole bag, but there are actually three servings on the label, you'll need to **triple** all of the numbers listed (calories, sugar, fat et al,) on the package. Serving sizes are relatively standard, which makes it easy to compare product labels for similar products to make healthier choices. Download your *Radical Label Reading Guide* in your virtual adventure toolkit this week to take a deeper dive on label reading.

TODAY: As you radically label read today, focus on **serving size**. Before you read the label, consider what you would normally consume for one serving. Are you aligned with the actual number of servings on the label? And don't stop with packaged goods. Check out the websites of some of the fast food and coffee chains you frequent. Knowledge is power.

REFLECTIONS:

WEEK #3 – DAY #13

AFFIRMATION: ***I am Confident!***

FOUNDATION/MEDITATION: "For the LORD will be **your confidence** and will keep your foot from being caught." *—Proverbs 3:26 (NKJV)*

"This is the **confidenc**e which we have before Him, that, if we ask anything according to His will, He hears us." *—1 John 5:14 (NIV)*

INSPIRATION: "If you have no confidence in self, you are twice defeated in the race of life." *—Marcus Garvey*

MOTIVATION: Let's look at a definition of confidence from Merriam-Webster: *1) the feeling or belief that one can rely on someone or something; firm trust. 2) a feeling of self-assurance arising from one's appreciation of one's own abilities or qualities.* Confidence is not conceit. Confidence is boldly taking ownership of your God-given gifts, talents and abilities and using them to serve the world. Be bold and courageous today! Head up and shoulders back—go get it!

PRAYER STARTER: *Thank you for this day. Help me to move boldly and confidently in purpose as I seek Your will and Your way. In Jesus' Name, Amen.*

ACTION: Radical Label Reading Challenge – Day #3

Sugar is basically sugar by any name. Research studies link added sugar to inflammation, which wreaks all kinds of havoc on your body. There are actually over 56 names for added sugar. It isn't uncommon for one packaged product to have multiple types of sugar in disguise on its labels, so you need to be a super sleuth. The USDA and the American Heart Association recommend 6 teaspoons of added sugar per day for women, and 9 for men. That's only 24 and 36 grams respectively. For perspective, one 12 oz. soda can have up to 39 grams of sugar.

TODAY: Be a relentless RLR for sugar today. Review the 56 names of sugar in your digital adventure toolkit this week. Scour your labels for popular sugars in disguise like dextrose, high-fructose corn syrup, maltose and maltodextrin. Check the sugar content of everything you eat today. You may be surprised where sugar is hiding in many of the packaged foods you enjoy regularly. Aim for single digit grams per serving, and compare products to find your healthiest options.

REFLECTIONS:

WEEK #3 – DAY #14

AFFIRMATION: ***I am Courageous!***

FOUNDATION/MEDITATION: "Be strong and **courageous.** Do not be afraid; do not be discouraged, for the LORD your God will be with you wherever you go." *—Joshua 1:9 (NIV)*

"Be on your guard; stand firm in the faith; **be courageous**; be strong." *—1 Corinthians 6:13 (NIV)*

INSPIRATION: "Courage is the most important of all the virtues because without courage, you can't practice any other virtue consistently." *—Maya Angelou*

MOTIVATION: Stretching outside of your comfort zone takes courage. I love the quote —"*The comfort zone is a beautiful place, but nothing ever grows there.*" It takes courage to live a healthier lifestyle when no one else is doing it around you. Be the courageous trailblazer that you are. And when others see your new energy, confidence and how good you look, just watch how they follow you to better health.

PRAYER STARTER: *Thank you for your Word. Help me to be bold and courageous today in my life and in the choices that I make for my whole-body health. In Jesus' Name, Amen.*

ACTION: Radical Label Reading Challenge – Day #4

Today we're going to focus on fiber! Fiber has so many benefits. In addition to keeping things moving internally, it also helps reduce your bad cholesterol, keeps you fuller longer and builds a healthier gut. Fiber is your partner when it comes to weight release and maintenance, so bulk up.

RLR Tip: Look for labels with at least a 10:1 carbohydrate to fiber ratio. **For every 10 grams of carbs on the label, look for at least 1g of fiber.**

TODAY: Put on your RLR detective hat and focus on fiber today. It's not uncommon for packaged and processed foods to have zero fiber. When it comes to flour, look for the word "whole" on the label. "Enriched" flour may sound like something good, but the fiber has actually been removed in the name of economics and shelf life. The impact of refined flour on your blood sugar is similar to that of added sugar. Your blood sugar spikes, crashes, and then you crave more sugary foods.

REFLECTIONS:

WEEK #3 – DAY #15

AFFIRMATION: ***I am Created to Do Good Works!***

FOUNDATION/MEDITATION: "For we are God's handiwork, **created in Christ Jesus to do good works**, which God prepared in advance for us to do." *—Ephesians 2:10 (NIV)*

INSPIRATION: "Your talent is God's gift to you. What you do with it is your gift back to God." *—Leo Buscaglia*

MOTIVATION: You were created on purpose to live in purpose. Even if you're not clear what it is, there is a unique seed of purpose inside of you—and it is good! Life can get in the way; things get busy, schedules run rampant, time flies and the next thing you know, you've lost connection with this God-given call. Prioritizing your health daily waters your seed of purpose by giving you more energy, clarity and creativity to understand and move in your call.

PRAYER STARTER: *Thank you for my life. Thank you for the reminder that my life has purpose. Speak to my heart and order my steps today. In Jesus' Name, Amen.*

ACTION: Radical Label Reading Challenge – Day #5

You made it to the end of this challenge! Remember your mantra—**"If God made it, eat it! If man made it, reduce it!"** Being a radical label reader is a lifestyle choice. And a great way to read fewer labels is to **cook more.** Home cooking is your declaration of independence from the Big Food industry hijacking your taste buds and your waistline.

TODAY: Continue your new RLR lifestyle practice this weekend and beyond. Compare products and make the healthiest choices. Look at ways to add more home cooking into your life. Follow a few healthy chefs on social media and check out their recipes. Consider exploring a new recipe each week. Make it a family affair and save everyone's favorite recipes in a folder (paper or digital) to add to your healthy food repertoire.

REFLECTIONS:

WEEK #4 – EAT WHEN YOU'RE HUNGRY CHALLENGE

"Better health begins at the end of your fork."

You're nearing the halfway point. You are showing up for yourself and I'm so ridiculously proud of you. Founder of the Institute of Integrative Nutrition, Joshua Rosenthal says, "*Food changes everything.*" What you eat today fuels your future. Before you put your fork in your mouth today and all week long, contemplate if what you're eating is giving you energy and life, or just short-term pleasure and long-term weight gain and fatigue. "*Choose Life!*" (Deuteronomy 30:19)

Consider what I call the **Intention Triad:**

Intention – Why am I eating? Is it hunger or something else?

Ingredients – What am I eating? (be a radical label reader)

Impact – How will what I'm eating impact my body? How will I feel a few hours from now and tomorrow?

ADVENTURE TOOLKIT

(Visit www.fitthrufaith.com for additional Week #4 resources and support)

- Camera or Camera Phone
- Food Diary (download from website)

WEEK #4 – DAY #16

AFFIRMATION: ***I am Fearless!***

FOUNDATION/MEDITATION: "Even though I walk through the darkest valley, **I will fear no evil,** for you are with me; your rod and your staff, they comfort me." *—Psalm 23:4 (NIV)*

"For God has **not given us a spirit of fear**, but of power and of love and of a sound mind."
—1 Timothy 1:7 (NKJV)

INSPIRATION: "Do one thing that scares you every day." *—Eleanor Roosevelt*

MOTIVATION: Being "fearless" is easier said than done, but you can shrink it down to size by releasing it spiritually and unpacking it in the natural. Fear is often the symptom of something deeper. Ask yourself questions to get to the root. What are you **really** afraid of? What's the worst thing that can happen if you push past it and get into action? God's got your back. Your front just needs to stay in action. Action is the antidote to fear. I like to say, "Action is sexy!"

PRAYER STARTER: *Thank you for the Holy Spirit that lives and dwells inside of me. Help me to release my fear and walk in your power today and always. In Jesus' Name, Amen.*

ACTION: Eat When You're Hungry Challenge – Day #1

This week's challenge sounds simple in concept, but it's not quite as easy as it sounds. Your body knows what it needs and when it needs it, but years of highly processed, convenient, and sugar-laden foods have created static in your communication system. This week you're going to work on clearing out some of that static.

TODAY: Starting today and for a minimum of 3 days, you're going to become a **photojournalist**. Take a quick shot of everything you eat and drink throughout the day. Download the **food diary template** in your adventure toolkit. You can also use a blank sheet of paper or make a spreadsheet on your computer. If you are DIY-ing it, write or type the following headers: **WHAT, WHY,** and **WHEN.** At the end of each day, fill in the columns with each meal, snack, or drink you enjoyed throughout the day.

Today, focus on the **WHAT** column. Take note. Is the food you're eating predominantly from God's buffet or man's? Any *aha* moments?

REFLECTIONS:

WEEK #4 – DAY #17

AFFIRMATION: ***I am Fearfully and Wonderfully Made!***

FOUNDATION/MEDITATION: "I praise you because I am **fearfully and wonderfully made**; your works are wonderful, I know that full well." *—Psalm 139:4 (NIV)*

INSPIRATION: "Beauty is being the best possible version of yourself." *—Audrey Hepburn*

MOTIVATION: Take a deep breath. Close your eyes. Inhale and truly embrace the fact that you are fearfully and wonderfully made. How does that make you feel? God crafted you perfectly. What you may see as a flaw may be exactly what God needs to bless someone through you and fulfill His purpose. So stop tearing yourself down, and more importantly, stop listening to words that don't speak life. My pastor says, "*Your life should reflect your relationship with God.*" My little remix is—"*Your health should reflect your relationship with God.*" As the Word says in I Corinthians 10:31 (NIV), "*So whether you eat or drink or whatever you do, do all for the glory of God.*" Your beauty and light radiate even brighter through a healthy temple.

PRAYER STARTER: *Thank you for how you uniquely created me. Help me to share my gifts and talents, as I eat and drink to your glory. In Jesus' Name, Amen.*

ACTION: Eat When You're Hungry Challenge – Day #2

Hunger is physical, and you know what it feels like. It's a gradual rolling sensation and a general feeling versus a specific desire. When you're hungry, you'll eat things that you don't even like that much to satisfy that physical need. So, if you have an immediate "need" for Häagen Dazs Cookies 'n Cream ice cream—it's not hunger. That's what we call a craving. But have no fear, cravings aren't necessarily a bad thing. **Cravings are a communication**. Your body is telling you it needs something, but the majority of the time it's not food. Dig a little deeper. Tap into what your body really needs. First and foremost, drink some water. You may be dehydrated. If you're bored—read a book or go for a walk. If you're lonely, call a friend, write in your journal, or go to a movie. Get into communication and connection with your body. Feed the real need, not the craving.

TODAY: Continue to snap photos and fill in your food journal or grid at the end of the day. Focus on the **WHY** column of your diary or grid today. Pay specific attention to your physical hunger signals. And if hunger isn't in the driver's seat, get to the root of what is and solve for that.

REFLECTIONS:

WEEK #4 – DAY #18

AFFIRMATION: ***I am Forgiven!***

FOUNDATION/MEDITATION: "But if we confess our sins to God, He will keep His promise and do what is right: He will **forgive** us our sins and purify us from all our wrongdoing." *—1 John 1:9 (NIV)*

"Get rid of all bitterness, rage and anger, brawling and slander, along with every form of malice. Be kind and compassionate to one another, forgiving each other, just as in Christ **God forgave you**."
—Ephesians 4:31-32 (NIV)

INSPIRATION: "Do not let the shadows of your past darken the doorstep of your future. Forgive and move on." *—Various*

MOTIVATION: It's truly time to let go and let God! Yes, you may have tried to release weight in the past and it has come back with friends, but it's time to repent, receive your refresh (Acts 3:19) and move on! It's time to forgive yourself for the self-sabotaging thoughts and behaviors and move boldly into your future fabulous self. Confess it, release it, and renew your commitment to better health.

PRAYER STARTER: *Thank you for loving me. Forgive me for not honoring my body, your temple, with my choices. Help me to make healthier choices today to your glory. In Jesus' Name, Amen.*

ACTION: Eat When You're Hungry Challenge – Day #3

This is the last "official" day of photo journaling, but I encourage you to continue the practice until you are fully present with your food choices. If you're eating the right amount and balance of food, you shouldn't be hungry for at least 3 hours. Your body actually needs the time to focus on digestion and switch from fat storing to fat burning. I call it the **power pause.** If you crunch and munch all day long, your body is continually in fat storing mode. Rest and digest so you can burn baby burn!

TODAY: Continue to photo journal, document, and review your diary or grid. Focus on the **WHEN** column. What time are you eating? How often are you eating? Do you see any patterns? Are you resting from eating for at least 3 hours between meals and/or snacks?

REFLECTIONS:

WEEK #4 – DAY #19

AFFIRMATION: *I am Free!*

FOUNDATION/MEDITATION: "So if the Son sets you free, **you will be free** indeed." *—John 8:36 (NIV)*

"Now the Lord is the Spirit, and where the Spirit of the Lord is, **there is freedom.**"
—2 Corinthians 3:17 (NIV)

INSPIRATION: "When I discover who I am, I'll be free." *—Ralph Ellison, "Invisible Man"*

MOTIVATION: When you discover and embrace who you are, and more importantly, whose you are, you experience true freedom. When you authentically receive, believe, and achieve these daily mantras, your mindset will begin to transform. Freedom from negative thoughts and food addictions is possible, but you must first reconnect with your power source. As the Word says in Psalms 127:1 (NIV), "*Unless the Lord builds the house, the builders labor in vain.*"

PRAYER STARTER: *Thank you for the freedom and power you've given me through the Holy Spirit. Help me to unleash that power to experience true freedom in my choices today. In Jesus' Name, Amen.*

ACTION: Eat When You're Hungry Challenge – Day #4

I encourage you to keep going with your food journal practice for the remainder of the week. And if you haven't started, today is a great day to start. Be mindful of your hand-to-mouth connection. In Brian Wansick's book, *"Mindless Eating,"* it states that we make over 200 eating decisions each day. 200! What environments, habits and triggers impact your mindless eating? What action steps can you take to solve for one of them today?

TODAY: Continue (or start) to photo journal and review your grid for aha moments. Do you see any patterns? Is there a certain time of the day or trigger that turns on your cravings?

REFLECTIONS:

WEEK #4 – DAY #20

AFFIRMATION: ***I am Free from Condemnation!***

FOUNDATION/MEDITATION: "There is therefore now **no condemnation** for those who are in Christ Jesus." —*Romans 8:1-2 ESV*

INSPIRATION: "The moment you asked for forgiveness, God forgave you. Now do your part and leave the guilt and shame behind." —*Unknown*

MOTIVATION: Max Lucado is quoted as saying, "*Guilt says, 'I made a mistake.' Shame says, 'I am a mistake.'*" God says, "*You are forgiven, free, and there is no condemnation.*" Fear, guilt and shame keep you from truly experiencing God's will for your health and your life. As I've said, I don't believe in "cheat days." Cheat days are guilt's playground. If guilt and shame are both playing on your swing set, run to the slide. One day of bingeing that goes unchecked can spiral into one week—and so on and so on. You are free from condemnation, so make choices that support your service to God and the world.

PRAYER STARTER: *Thank you for the reminder that there is no condemnation. Help me to release my negative self-talk to embrace who I am in you. In Jesus' Name, Amen.*

ACTION: Eat When You're Hungry Challenge – Day #5

You made it to Day #5 of the challenge! If you want to go the distance, photo journal into the weekend. Weekends can be a challenge to your healthy lifestyle because your schedule is usually more flexible and there's less structure and more free time. More free time can lead to more free eating. Collect all of the data you can. Self-examine. Mindfulness and connection with **what, when, and why** you're eating can make a big difference in the way you look, feel and serve.

TODAY: Continue to photo journal into the weekend. What are you learning to help you make better choices for your whole-body health?

REFLECTIONS:

HALFWAY THERE!

You're halfway to a new you! Let's take a moment to CELEBRATE your journey.

What are your biggest take-aways and revelations so far?

____

____

____

____

____

____

What obstacles/challenges have you been experiencing these past few weeks?

____

____

____

____

____

____

What strategies can you use to overcome these obstacles to be even more successful in the last 20 days?

____

____

____

____

Now let's check in with your **intention.** Review your intention statement from the beginning of your adventure. Do you need to make any adjustments? If so, rewrite your statement below.

____

____

____

____

____

____

____

____

Now before we move on, I do have a tough love question to ask you. Consider the following quote:

"If you're interested,
you will do what's convenient.
If you're committed,
you'll do whatever it takes."

– Joseph Assaraf

My question for you is **"Are you committed or just interested in being of greater service to God and the world?"** If you're truly committed, then it's time to do whatever it takes to be in better whole-body health.

WEEK #5 – 'BOUT THAT VEGGIE LIFE CHALLENGE

"Whole plant-based foods are God's heart insurance."

Now that your intention is strong, what are you going to do differently in the back half of this adventure to finish strong? If you want to support your heart health, eat more plant-based foods—the more colorful your plate the better. The Center for Disease Control has reported that 90 percent of Americans don't get enough vegetables, fruit and fiber—and then we wonder why diet-related diseases are a leading cause of death in this country. Not to sound like a broken record but eating more of the nutrient-dense healing foods that God created for you to enjoy and excel is a simple way to have an immediate impact on your heart health.

You are a Rolls Royce. Stop fueling your temple like a used Cutlass with cheap, low-octane, knock-off gas that clogs you up and slows you down. It's time to upgrade to the premium fuel from God's abundant buffet. This is the food that really "does a body good."

ADVENTURE TOOLKIT

(Visit www.fitthrufaith.com for Week #5 resources and support)

WEEK #5 – DAY #21

AFFIRMATION: ***I am Healed!***

FOUNDATION/MEDITATION: "Behold, I will bring to it health and **healing**, and I will **heal** them and reveal to them abundance of prosperity and security." *—Jeremiah 33:6*

INSPIRATION: "Healthy Self, Heal Thyself." *—Unknown*

MOTIVATION: God crafted your body as a perfect bio-computer. It knows how to maintain your temperature at 98.6 degrees, how to fight off infection, and most importantly, how to heal itself. You support and protect the intricate transmissions of this complex bio-computer when you fuel up with the health-giving and healing foods that God created. If the cornerstone of your diet is man-made, processed and lab-created faux food, chronic inflammation and disease build. But the beautiful thing is, through making healthier choices over time, you can prevent and even reverse disease. Be mindful of how you fill your plate today.

PRAYER STARTER: *Thank you for your healing power. Help me to make food choices today that support my health and healing. In Jesus' Name, Amen.*

ACTION: 'Bout that Veggie Life Challenge – Day #1

You're drinking water, reading labels, staying active and eating when you're hungry. Woo hoo! You've come a long way. Now that you're connected with what you're eating, it's time to power up the plant-based foods in your life. **"Veggies first!"** is your new mantra. There are five basic color groups, each with a unique bundle of nutrient goodness, that we'll break down this week.

TODAY: The color is **green**. In addition to being my favorite color, green veggies are power packed with vitamins A, C, E and K, as well as folate and calcium, among other nutrients. They help you look good, feel good and support your immune health and vitality. Make a list today of the green veggies and fruits you love, and get in as many servings today as possible.

How about a "Green Leafy Goodness" (GLG) smoothie? Download the recipe for my starter **Basic One** from your toolkit. And once you're happy with the basic recipe, you can boost it up. Some of my favorite boosts are organic pea protein powder, cacao powder, maca powder, cinnamon, turmeric, flax meal and avocado.

REFLECTIONS:

WEEK #5 – DAY #22

AFFIRMATION: *I am His Child!*

FOUNDATION/MEDITATION: "So in Christ Jesus you are all **children of God** through faith." *—Galatians 3:26 (NIV)*

INSPIRATION: "You are not who people say you are. You are who God says you are. You are a child of God." *—Unknown*

MOTIVATION: Your relationship (or lack thereof) with your father can have a profound impact on your sense of self and how you relate to and interact with people and the world. Whether your dad was very present or absent, you can rest in the fact that your Heavenly Father thinks you're pretty terrific. You are His beautiful child. You are His creation and He is well pleased. When you're in doubt and the negative chatter starts to get loud, go back and meditate on the mantras and scriptures in this book. Remind yourself what your Heavenly Father says about you and all that you are capable of accomplishing.

PRAYER STARTER: *Thank you for saving me. I am your child. Help me to make you proud of the food and fitness choices that I make today. In Jesus' Name, Amen.*

ACTION: 'Bout that Veggie Life Challenge – Day #2

The U.S.D.A. recommends 5–9 servings of veggies and fruit each day, which may seem daunting. It's not so hard when you focus on "**Veggies First!**" Starting your morning with a GLG smoothie will jumpstart 2–4 servings. Create a scrumptious super salad at lunch for another 3–4 servings. Add in a whole fruit or veggie snack, and finish your evening with a side salad and roasted veggies with dinner. Done!

TODAY: The color is **red**. Make a list of the red veggies and fruits you love. Which ones have been missing from your grocery cart lately? Invite them back into your life. The rich antioxidants in red veggies support heart and blood health, among other things. How many servings of red veggies can you get in today?

REFLECTIONS:

WEEK #5 – DAY #23

AFFIRMATION: ***I am His Handiwork!***

FOUNDATION/MEDITATION: "For we are **God's handiwork**, created in Christ Jesus to do good works, which God prepared in advance for us to do." *—Ephesians 2:10 (NIV)*

INSPIRATION: "If you want to know God's best creation, just see it in the mirror." *—Ankivet V. Deshmukh*

MOTIVATION: Who's your favorite artist? How do you define great art? For me, a great piece of art is one that you can look at over and over again and see something new, beautiful, complex, thought provoking and inspiring each time. You are God's masterpiece. What do you see when you look in the mirror? Do you see the perfection of His brush stroke in your delicate features, the craftsmanship of your bone structure, the beauty of your curves, and the complexity of the organs that give you breath and life? Do you see the power of your possibilities, your promise, and your purpose? If not—look again—and again, and again! See yourself today in a fresh new way. Marvel at God's glorious creation!

PRAYER STARTER: *Thank you for uniquely crafting me in your image. Help me see the beauty of your creation in the mirror today. In Jesus' Name, Amen.*

ACTION: 'Bout that Veggie Life Challenge – Day #3

The concept of "crowding out" is a gentle process towards healthier eating. Instead of removing all of the "bad things" that you enjoy, focus on adding in more plant-based foods like veggies, fruits, legumes, and whole kernel grains. With more of these nutritious and delicious powerhouses in your life, the man-made processed foods that seed inflammation and disease in your body are naturally "crowded out."

TODAY: The color group is **orange/yellow**—two colors with a rich variety of flavors and textures to explore. Make a list of the orange/yellow veggies and fruits you love. The Vitamin C and beta-carotene in these foods support your eye health and immune system, as well as healthy hair and skin. How many servings of orange/yellow veggies can you get in today? Sweet potatoes anyone?

REFLECTIONS:

WEEK #5 – DAY #24

AFFIRMATION: ***I am Holy!***

FOUNDATION/MEDITATION: "But just as he who called you is holy, so **be holy** in all you do; for it is written: "Be holy, because I am holy." *—1 Peter 1:15-16 (NIV)*

INSPIRATION: "There are no shortcuts to spiritual maturity. It takes time to be holy." *—Erwin W. Lutzer*

MOTIVATION: Holiness is a journey of being mindful that your thoughts, words, and actions line up with the Word of God. After all, it's called the "Holy" Bible. Reading and meditating on the Word daily supports the very foundation of your whole-body health. Whatever challenge you are facing today, seek Him first. "*Take captive every thought to make it obedient to Christ*" (2 Corinthians 10:5 NIV).

PRAYER STARTER: *Thank you for your Word of instruction, inspiration and correction. Help me to walk in holiness today in my thoughts, words and actions. In Jesus' Name, Amen.*

ACTION: 'Bout that Veggie Life Challenge – Day #4

Your plate is getting more colorful by the day. The "**Veggies First**!" mantra isn't just about powering up your veggies, but also eating them first in each meal. Veggies are naturally low in calories, so you begin to fill up on the food with the least calories and the most nutrition first. #winning

TODAY: The color group is **blue/purple**. The antioxidants from these beauties support mental clarity and longevity. Make your list and enjoy. Check out your local farmer's market this weekend to find naturally occurring purple-hued cauliflower, broccoli, carrots, and sweet potatoes. Yum!

REFLECTIONS:

WEEK #5 – DAY #25

AFFIRMATION: ***I am Light!***

FOUNDATION/MEDITATION: "You are the **light** of the world. A town built on a hill cannot be hidden. Neither do people light a lamp and put it under a bowl. Instead they put it on its stand, and it gives light to everyone in the house. In the same way, **let your light shine** before others, that they may see your good deeds and glorify your Father in heaven." *—Matthew 5:14-16 (NIV)*

INSPIRATION: "It is our **light,** not our darkness, that most frightens us. We ask ourselves, who am I to be brilliant, gorgeous, talented and fabulous? Actually, who are you not to be? You are a child of God..." *—Marianne Williamson*

MOTIVATION: Matthew 5:16 is my life verse. Each and every day I strive to be light in my walk, talk, and actions. I don't always succeed, but it's my heart's desire. My grandmother, the late Julma Brown Crawford, is the founder of the Debutante Master Commission in the A.M.E. Church. I grew up on their motto, "*Daily Magnify Christ.*" But it wasn't until I was an adult that I understood the power of putting those words into practice. How can you let your light shine a little brighter to radiate and magnify Christ in your life today?

PRAYER STARTER: *Thank you for your light. Help me to be light today, so others might see you through my thoughts, words and actions. And I will be sure to give you all the glory. In Jesus' Name, Amen.*

ACTION: 'Bout that Veggie Life Challenge – Day #5

Last but not least, we're going to highlight the color family that is often overlooked. The **white/tan** color group brings its own unique super powers to your plate. Several white/tan veggies contain the antioxidant allicin (found in onions), which plays a role in your heart health, and cholesterol maintenance. And now that you've had a chance to play with all of the colors in God's crayon box, look at your plate as a blank canvas. Be creative and enjoy using the various color groups to paint a colorful and yummy plate for each meal this weekend and moving forward.

TODAY: It's time to rice your cauliflower, roast your onions and garlic, sauté a medley of mushrooms, crunch on some jicama, or pop a frozen banana into your smoothie. How can you get more white/tan produce in today?

REFLECTIONS:

WEEK #6 – 10-MINUTE WORKOUT CHALLENGE

"The only bad workout is the one that never happened."

When I was pledging my sorority in college, we had to memorize the following quote:

"Excuses are tools of the incompetent.
They build monuments of nothingness, and
Those who specialize in them seldom
accomplish anything."
—Author Unknown

Those words always come back to me when I hear myself (or my children) making excuses—even when it's "constructive" procrastination. As you near these final weeks of this adventure, make a conscious effort to excuse-proof your health. "I don't have time!" is a top excuse from my clients for not doing what they know they need to do. The reality is that you do have time. You just haven't made the decision to prioritize your health. You make time for the activities that are important to you. Some physical activity is better than none, so determine how much time you do have and be consistent. This week, you're going to prove to yourself that you have at least 10 minutes each day to show your heart, bones and muscles some love.

ADVENTURE TOOLKIT

(Visit www.fitthrufaith.com for Week #6 resources and support)

WEEK #6 – DAY #26

AFFIRMATION: ***I am Loved!***

FOUNDATION/MEDITATION: "For God so **loved** the world that he gave his one and only Son, that whoever believes in him shall not perish but have eternal life." *—John 3:16 (NIV)*

"The Lord appeared to us in the past, saying: "**I have loved you with an everlasting love**; I have drawn you with unfailing kindness."
—Jeremiah 31:3 (NIV)

INSPIRATION: "God loves each of us as if there were only one of us." *—Augustine*

MOTIVATION: You are loved! No matter what choices you made yesterday—you are loved! Seeing yourself and loving yourself as God does is the beginning of your whole-body health adventure. When you look in the mirror, what emotions do you feel? If love isn't one of them, you have some work to do. What is standing in the way of you loving yourself as God does? Unpack it. What lies have others told you about yourself that you've accepted? If the chatter in your head doesn't line up with the Word of God, release it! What's one step you can take to love yourself more today? As Stephen Covey says, "*Love is a verb.*" Love requires action.

PRAYER STARTER: *Thank you for loving me with an everlasting love. Show me your way to love myself more today. In Jesus' Name, Amen.*

ACTION: 10-Minute Workout Challenge – Day #1

Did you know that only 10 minutes of continuous movement can benefit your heart? Well it's true—just 10 minutes! And if you don't have 10 minutes in your schedule, you may need to reevaluate how you are investing your time. You still want to aim for the recommended 30 minutes per day, but you can do it in 10-minute increments. If you haven't been getting regular exercise, what has been blocking you? Call it out. If you don't "like" working, then you haven't connected with something you enjoy. Be a problem solver. Physical fitness is not optional when it comes to making your epic impact on this world.

TODAY: Check out this week's toolkit for a variety of 10-minute videos to try, but feel free to Google "10-Minute Workout" or checkout your app store to find others. Pick a workout that intrigues you and get into action. And if online videos and apps aren't your thing, go for a walk or blast your favorite playlist for a spontaneous dance party.

REFLECTIONS:

WEEK #6 – DAY #27

AFFIRMATION: ***I am Made in His Image!***

FOUNDATION/MEDITATION: "So God **created mankind in his own image**, in the image of God he created them; male and female he created them." *—Genesis 1:27 (NIV)*

INSPIRATION: "Who taught you to hate being what God made you?" *—Malcolm X*

MOTIVATION: You were crafted with love in the image of God, so how do you think God feels when you look in the mirror with disappointment or disapproval? I imagine that it's like being the first person in a relationship to blurt out, "I love you," and getting "crickets" as a response. When you step in front of the mirror, God is saying, "I love you. I love you!" What is your response? Start by just "assuming the position." Your reflection is your partner in this whole-body health adventure. Start each day by saying, "I love you" back until you really mean it.

PRAYER STARTER: *Thank you for crafting me in your image. Help me quiet down the negative chatter and see more of you through my reflection in the mirror today. In Jesus' Name, Amen.*

ACTION: 10-Minute Workout Challenge – Day #2

When is the best time to work out? The time when you are least likely to be distracted. Yes, there are some additional benefits to morning workouts, but if you're just not a morning workout person, those benefits are useless. Schedule your 10 minutes for the rest of the week. Put it in your calendar. The goal is to establish consistency, 10 minutes at a time.

TODAY: Do the same video or try a new one today. Go for a hall walk, do some laps around the house, or get outside to walk around at lunch. Calendar it. Commit to it. Celebrate it!

REFLECTIONS:

WEEK #6 – DAY #28

AFFIRMATION: ***I am more than a Conqueror***

FOUNDATION/MEDITATION: "Yet in all these things we are **more than conquerors** through Him who loved us." *—Romans 8:37 (NKJV)*

INSPIRATION: "You may suffer many defeats in life, but you will not be defeated. You will rise after every trial stronger and wiser." *—Leon Brown*

MOTIVATION: According to the Bible, you are not just a conqueror, you are MORE than a conqueror. Merriam-Webster Definition: *one who conquers, one who wins a country in war, subdues or subjugates a people or overcomes an adversary.* Who or what is your adversary? Is it a person, place, or thing? What or who is standing in the way of your better health? Time, self-esteem, your negative chatter, job stress, your spouse, or perhaps your ex? Digging deeper may not feel good, but it's the work that leads to transformation. Call out your adversary. Make a plan and determine the first thing that you can do to subdue it. The battle is already won, but you have to step onto the battlefield and take action to experience your victory.

PRAYER STARTER: *Thank you for the conquering spirit that burns inside of me. Reveal those things, people and feelings today that are standing in the way of my better whole-body health. Help me to conquer and root them out to your glory. In Jesus' Name, Amen.*

ACTION: 10-Minute Workout Challenge – Day #3

The positive impact of exercise on your heart is well known, but there's also mounting evidence of the positive impact it can have on your brain health as well. It actually makes sense when you think about it, as both organs need the same healthy blood flow. More studies are listing physical activity high on the list for Alzheimer's prevention. Brain fog is real, but you can do something about it. The more you exercise, the greater the benefits, but anything is better than nothing. Get up 10 minutes early or wind down 10 minutes earlier at night.

By the way, are your workouts scheduled for the remainder of the week? If not, get them in your calendar. Show up for yourself and reap the benefits of more energy, clearer thoughts and a healthier heart.

TODAY: Try a new 10-minute video from your adventure toolkit suggestions, the web or your favorite fitness app. If you have time to go to the gym or get outside for a quick hike—go for it!

REFLECTIONS:

WEEK #6 – DAY #29

AFFIRMATION: *I am New!*

FOUNDATION/MEDITATION: "If anyone is in Christ, the new creature has come. The old has gone, the new is here!" *—2 Corinthians 5:17 (NIV)*

INSPIRATION: "It's a new dawn. It's a new day. I'm feeling good." *—Nina Simone*

MOTIVATION: Your walk is not one of perfection, but one of progress. Each day seek God's better in your life. Seeking perfection can be defeating—and who wants that? Each sunrise brings a new opportunity and possibility to be more and serve more. Leave yesterday's disappointments and frustrations behind. Begin to act the part of a healthier person today. Drink your lemon water. Read your labels. Eat more veggies and move your body. And after today's success, do it again tomorrow until it becomes a habit. Enjoy the journey!

PRAYER STARTER: *It's a new day. This is a day that You have made, and I will rejoice and be glad in it. Help me to leave the events, thoughts and choices of yesterday in the past and embrace a clean slate to make healthier choices today. In Jesus' Name, Amen.*

ACTION: 10-Minute Workout Challenge – Day #4

How's it going? 10 minutes is doable. Right? This is a great time to debrief on your success strategy. How are you making it happen? What choices are you making to ensure your success? And if you've been struggling to make time, look at your obstacles. What are the top two blockers standing in the way of your success? Write them down and problem solve for the success you will experience tomorrow.

TODAY: If you're enjoying your current video or routine, then stick with it. If you need to mix it up a little, then try something new. Just stay committed and consistent. Create accountability by asking a family member or friend to join in.

REFLECTIONS:

WEEK #6 – DAY #30

AFFIRMATION: *I am Peaceful!*

FOUNDATION/MEDITATION: "You will keep in **perfect peace** those whose minds are steadfast, because they trust in you." *—Isaiah 26:3 (NKJV)*

"**Peace** I leave with you, my peace I give to you; not as the world gives do I give to you. Let not your heart be troubled, neither let it be afraid."
—John 14:27 (NKJV)

INSPIRATION: Ego says, "Once everything falls into place, I'll feel peace." Spirit says, "Find your peace, and then everything will fall into place." — *Marianne Williamson*

MOTIVATION: You are filled with peace. I love the verse above from Isaiah 26:3. It's God's instant prescription for peace. If you're feeling fear, anxiety, anger, or frustration today, shift your thoughts heavenward. If your mind or your mouth are not feeling very peaceful, breathe. Put your feet flat on the floor with your right hand on heart and your left on your belly. Breathe in deeply from your belly through your nose as you gently close your eyes (think 4 counts). Hold your breath slightly at the top and then slowly exhale through your mouth. Focus on each breath and how your body is feeling. Your mind will want to wander, but gently focus it back on your breath. With each exhale focus on the goodness of God. If a scripture comes to mind, stay with it and repeat it in your mind. After four good, deep breaths, open your eyes and go slay the day! Before you get moving each day, connect with the source of your peace, strength, and joy.

PRAYER STARTER: *Thank you for your peace. Help me keep my mind focused on you today. When fear, uncertainty, doubt and negativity surround me, help me to turn down those voices and focus on you. In Jesus' Name, Amen.*

ACTION: 10-Minute Workout Challenge – Day #5

This may be the last day of this challenge, but you've only just begun. My prayer is that you've experienced how successful you can be at building a behavior of daily activity, but don't stop here. Keep up the great work into the weekend and beyond by extending your time each week by 5–10 minutes. Be adventurous and find an online coupon or discount for a local gym, boot camp or dance exercise class. Remind your body each day how much you love and need it by getting your heart and muscles moving daily.

TODAY: Go back to one of the videos you love or try a new one. If you've been doing cardio, try strength training. If you've been strength training, try a cardio workout. Variety is what keeps your physical activity practice interesting, exciting, and lasting. If you're a mom with kids who play sports, get a few laps in while they practice or find some family fun time to take a walk, ride bikes, or go for a hike.

REFLECTIONS:

WEEK #7 – CHEW CHALLENGE

"Behave your way to better health."

It's hard to believe that we're in the final two weeks of your 40-day journey. This is the time to dig in even more to finish strong. Your health is the sum of your thoughts, choices and behaviors around **faith, food and fitness**. You know what you need to do, but are your behaviors lining up with what you know you need to do? For example: You know you need to eat more veggies. What behavior is standing in the way? Call it out and build an action plan to course correct it in a healthier direction. You can begin with your grocery list for this week. You know what a healthier version of you should look like. Take action steps and act the part until it lines up with your reality.

ADVENTURE TOOLKIT

(Visit www.fitthrufaith.com for Week #7 resources and support)

WEEK #7 – DAY #31

AFFIRMATION: ***I am Powerful!***

FOUNDATION/MEDITATION: "But you will receive **power** when the Holy Spirit comes on you; and you will be my witnesses in Jerusalem, and in all Judea and Samaria, and to the ends of the earth." *—Acts 1:8 (NIV)*

INSPIRATION: "Being powerful is like being a lady. If you have to tell people that you are, you aren't." *—Margaret Thatcher*

MOTIVATION: What is your super power? You have one. God has uniquely gifted you with a super natural ability. Here's a hint: think back to your childhood. What was your super power then? It may be a spiritual gift or talent, or perhaps the ability to make people laugh or smile. Own and acknowledge your super power today. What is your theme music? If you don't have a theme song yet, get one. How can you make the world a better place by exercising your super power today?

PRAYER STARTER: *Thank you for the power you have given me through the Holy Spirit. Help me to exercise that power to push past those things that are blocking me from living in better health. In Jesus' Name, Amen.*

ACTION: Chew Challenge – Day #1

Chewing your food—I mean really chewing your food—is a simple path to a healthier you. There are multiple benefits to thoroughly chewing your food. Number one, it supports healthy digestion, which ultimately impacts the way you look, feel, and serve. Digestion starts in your mouth. When you chew your food thoroughly, you give the digestive enzymes in your mouth time to do their job and to signal to all the other organs to get ready to do their jobs. Your stomach doesn't have teeth after all, so give it a little support.

TODAY: Let's get into connection with your chewing today by being mindful about the number of chews you take per bite and the amount of time it takes for you to complete each meal. Jot down your average daily numbers.

REFLECTIONS:

WEEK #7 – DAY #32

AFFIRMATION: ***I am Qualified!***

FOUNDATION/MEDITATION: "Giving joyful thanks to the Father, who has qualified you to share in the inheritance of his people in the kingdom of light." —*Colossians 1:12 (NIV)*

INSPIRATION: "Be yourself. No one is better qualified." —*Unknown*

MOTIVATION: If God called you to do it, you are qualified—whether you believe it or not. Own that job promotion or new role, even though the nay-sayers and your inner critic are questioning your ability. If the call that God has on your life feels too big, don't get overwhelmed by it. Being over-whelmed can cloud your vision and stop your prog-ress. Instead, focus on 1–3 action steps that you can do each day until the task is done. Be realistic, schedule time to do it, and marvel at all you can accomplish when you focus on action. It won't be long until you actually believe that you are qualified to do what God has called you to do.

PRAYER STARTER: *Thank you for qualifying me to share in your inheritance. Thank you for the call you have on my life. I am qualified to fulfill it through you. Reveal the steps I need to take today and order them in your Word (Psalms 119:33). In Jesus' Name, Amen.*

ACTION: Chew Challenge – Day #2

Now that you're mindful about your chewing, let's go deeper. There's a proverb that says, "*Drink your food and chew your liquid.*" I love the imagery, because ultimately you want to chew your food down to a paste or liquid. Another benefit of chewing is that it allows your body to better absorb nutrients. If you're making time to eat healthier, don't leave money on the table. The more work you do in your mouth, the more available those nutrients will be for your cells to give you the energy you need for the day.

TODAY: Now that you know your average chew number, try adding 10 chews to each bite today. Obviously, some foods need more or less, but be mindful of **chewing more** today.

REFLECTIONS:

WEEK #7 – DAY #33

AFFIRMATION: ***I am Redeemed!***

FOUNDATION/MEDITATION: "In him we have **redemption** through his blood, the forgiveness of our trespasses, according to the riches of his grace." *—Ephesians 1:7 (NIV)*

"He has delivered us from the domain of darkness and transferred us to the kingdom of his beloved Son, in whom we have **redemption**, the forgiveness of sins."

—Colossians 1:13-14 (NIV)

INSPIRATION: "People, even more than things, have to be restored, renewed, revived, reclaimed, and redeemed; never throw out anyone." *—Audrey Hepburn*

MOTIVATION: Redeemed feels like a powerful word, because it is. All the "stuff" that you did, said, or thought in the past has been handled and paid for—so let it go. You're saved and safe. When your inner critic is whispering negative things in your ear or keeping you stuck in the past, remind yourself who and whose you are. Turn down the static and turn up WGOD—*"Whatsoever things are true, whatever things are honest, whatever things* *are just, pure...lovely...of good report...if there be any virtue, if there be any praise, think on these things." —Philippians 4:8 (KJV)*

PRAYER STARTER: *Thank you for your redemption. Help me today to walk in that power. Help me turn down the negative chatter and turn up WGOD to embrace all that is true, honest, just, pure, lovely and of good report in my life. In Jesus' Name, Amen.*

ACTION: Chew Challenge – Day #3

Day #3 is here! How's it going? Admittedly, the chewing thing was hard for me because I used to be a card carrying fast eater. But now, I can't imagine going back to racing through chewing because of the positive impact it has had on my waistline. Chewing your food thoroughly naturally slows down the eating process. It takes 20 minutes for your brain to register that your body is full. If you're eating too fast, you might be on your second plate before you even know if you're still hungry. Chewing is a great way to truly "eat when you're hungry," and curb mindless overeating.

TODAY: Let's go for at least 20 chews per bite. And even if you don't hit that mark for every bite, get a sense of what it feels like to chew your food down to a liquid-ish state.

REFLECTIONS:

WEEK #7 – DAY #34

AFFIRMATION: ***I am Royalty!***

FOUNDATION/MEDITATION: "But you are a chosen race, a **royal priesthood,** a holy nation, a people for his own possession, that you may proclaim the excellency of him who called you out of darkness into his marvelous light." *—1 Peter 2:9 (ESV)*

INSPIRATION: "Think like a queen. A queen is not afraid to fail. Failure is another stepping stone to greatness." *—Oprah*

MOTIVATION: You are royalty, so stand tall today. A small shift in your posture can make a big shift in your confidence, as well as how you look and feel. Hold your head up high today, shoulders back, crown lifted, and stroll with pride. Be a royal snob about the food that you put into your temple. Lean on the whole clean foods that God created for you to survive and thrive. You're too royal for lab-created artificial ingredients and processed foods that slow you down and clog you up. Embrace your lineage today. You are a child of the Most High King.

PRAYER STARTER: *Thank you for reminding me that I am royalty. Help me to represent you well today in my walk, talk and choices. In Jesus' Name, Amen.*

ACTION: Chew Challenge – Day #4

It's Day #4! You're starting to get into a rhythm with this chewing thing. Research has also linked increased chewing to brain and gum health. Studies have shown chewing helps maintain cognition in the part of your brain that's responsible for memory and learning. Your teeth and gums also benefit from the extra saliva that chewing produces to wash away food particles and bacteria. It's a two-for-one!

TODAY: Work up to 30 chews per bite today as a guide. Some foods will ultimately require more and some less. Mindfulness is the key this week. It does take time for this practice to become a habit, so be kind to yourself. You've been chewing too quickly for decades, so be patient. It took a few months for this habit to become automatic for me, and I still have to catch myself from time to time.

REFLECTIONS:

WEEK #7 – DAY #35

AFFIRMATION: *I am Secure!*

FOUNDATION/MEDITATION: "And you will feel secure, because there is hope; you will look around and take your rest in security." *—Job 11:18 (ESV)*

"I have set the Lord always before me; because he is at my right hand, I shall not be shaken."
—Psalm 16:8 (ESV)

INSPIRATION: "God made you a masterpiece—be blessed, secure, disciplined and equipped."
—Joel Osteen

MOTIVATION: Insecurity implies what I call F.U.D.—fear, uncertainty and doubt. You certainly know by now, verse by verse, that none of those "feelings" are biblical. In fact, just the opposite. Take a deeper look. If you are having feelings of fear and doubt about your ability to live a healthier and happier life, what is at the root? And if you don't know, keep digging. The solution is inside of you. Whatever it is, write it out, acknowledge it, and flip the script to speak life!

PRAYER STARTER: *Thank you for your hope and your purpose. Help me to embrace your security in my future as I strive to make healthier choices today. In Jesus' Name, Amen.*

ACTION: Chew Challenge – Day #5
Last and certainly not least, another important reason to chew more is to enjoy your food. The Word says in 3 John 1:2 (NIV) to "**enjoy** good health." God created an abundant buffet of yummy goodness for you to enjoy. If you eat too fast, you miss the layers of flavors and textures. Slow down and savor each bite. And if you're not enjoying your food, stop chewing it. There's no need to waste the calories on food you don't enjoy.

TODAY: The goal today is to transform eating into an experience. Carve time and savor each bite. What flavors and textures do you notice? And if you aren't noticing anything, what do you need to add the next time? Chewing your food to a liquid can truly have an impact on a healthier body and slimmer waistline, so keep up the great work from this day forward.

REFLECTIONS:

WEEK #8 – SUGAR-FREE(DOM) CHALLENGE

"Eat less sugar. You're sweet enough already."

Week 8 is here! This is a great time to go back and look at your intention statement. On a scale of 1–10, where are you? If your number doesn't bring you joy, what number are you shooting for this week? This week's challenge can be one of the harder shifts to make, but it can also be the most impactful. I'm talking about added and artificial sugar. Must we? Yes!

Why? Because excess sugar fuels preventable chronic diseases like obesity, Type 2 diabetes, and heart disease. Yes, it tastes good, but it's also slowly but surely stealing your energy and vitality. Sugar also lights up the same part of the brain as cocaine, so the impact is real. Eating less or removing added sugar may seem impossible, but once you experience the benefits of a slimmer waist, clearer thinking and more energy, you will be glad you did.

ADVENTURE TOOLKIT

(Visit www.fitthrufaith.com for Week #8 resources and support)

WEEK 8 – DAY #36

AFFIRMATION: ***I am Strong!***

FOUNDATION/MEDITATION: "Be **strong** in the Lord and in the power of His might." *—Ephesians 6:10 (KJV)*

INSPIRATION: "Deny your weakness, and you will never realize God's strength in you." *—Joni Eareckson Toda*

MOTIVATION: I named my fitness brand "Proverbs 31 Body" because Proverbs 31:25 (NIV) says, "*She is clothed with strength and dignity; she can laugh at the days to come.*" When you embrace your strength, both spiritually and physically, you can smile and laugh at your future because you know it is filled with God's promises and purpose. Make a plan each day to build up your physical and spiritual strength to be in a ready position to be blessed and to be a blessing to those around you.

PRAYER STARTER: *Thank you for your strength and your power. Help me to embrace your strength today in my thoughts and actions as I walk boldly in the call you have on my life. In Jesus' Name, Amen.*

ACTION: Sugar-Free(dom) Challenge – Day #1

Let's end strong! Reducing added sugar in your diet is one of the most impactful things you can do for a healthier you. Plus, you'll have younger looking skin, a happier waistline and a healthier heart. This week is about getting into connection with your relationship with sugar.

TODAY: Let's begin to connect with the sugar in your life. As you learned in the Radical Label Reading Challenge, there are over 56 names of sugar. Read those labels and aim for single digits in the sugar line. Where is the added sugar showing up in your daily diet? Check out your adventure toolkit this week for some healthier sweet swaps.

REFLECTIONS:

WEEK #8 – DAY #37

AFFIRMATION: ***I am the Apple of His Eye!***

FOUNDATION/MEDITATION: "Keep me as the **apple of the eye**, hide me under the shadow of thy wings." *—Psalm 17:8 (KJV)*

"For thus says the LORD of hosts, 'After glory He has sent me against the nations which plunder you, for he who touches you, touches **the apple of His eye**.'" *—Zechariah 2:8 (NIV)*

INSPIRATION: "You are the sunshine of my life, that's why I'll always be around. You are the apple of my eye. Forever you'll stay in my heart." *—Stevie Wonder*

MOTIVATION: If you're hearing Stevie Wonder's voice in your head right now, enjoy it. That is exactly how God thinks of you. You are the sunshine of His life and the apple of His eye. Don't let the world and people define you with words and labels that aren't even true. Own your true worth.

PRAYER STARTER: *Thank you for loving me as only you can. Help me to continue to see myself through your eyes. In Jesus' Name, Amen.*

ACTION: Sugar-Free(dom) Challenge – Day #2

Liquid sugar is a perfect place to start reducing added sugar in your life. Your brain actually registers these calories differently than solid food. When you drink calories, your brain doesn't signal fullness the same way, so you end up potentially eating more food and calories.

TODAY: Let's go sugar-free in your drink choices today. Yes, it may sound like a big ask, but try it. What can you have? Water (and lots of it—even the sparkling kind), green and herbal tea, coffee with cinnamon or unsweetened almond milk, kombucha (with no added sugar—check the label). You can do this!

REFLECTIONS:

WEEK #8 – DAY #38

AFFIRMATION: ***I am Triumphant!***

FOUNDATION/MEDITATION: "But thanks be to God, who in Christ always leads us in **triumphal** procession, and through us spreads the fragrance of the knowledge of him everywhere." *—2 Corinthians 2:14 (ESV)*

INSPIRATION: "I learned that courage was not the absence of fear, but the triumph over it." *—Nelson Mandela*

MOTIVATION: What is standing in the way of you being triumphant in your whole-body health? Call it out. Plug into your **Big Bold Why** today. Remind yourself why you need to be in better health. Your BBW should be fueled by your passion to leave a legacy and make your epic impact on this world. What difference can you make in someone else's life today? Write down one action step you can take and complete it.

PRAYER STARTER: *Thank you for your triumphant spirit. Reveal the things today that are blocking my brilliance, my message and my call. Give me the power to triumph over them to be of greater service to you and this world. In Jesus' Name, Amen.*

ACTION: Sugar-Free(dom) Challenge – Day #3

Your breakfast plate can be a compass for how you will feel all day long. Skipping this first important meal or breaking your fast with foods that are high in sugar and low in fiber (processed cereals, donuts, bagels, fruit juices, etc.) early in the day sets you up for a sugar roller coaster. You'll feel energized when your blood sugar spikes, but a few hours later, you'll crash and crave more sugary and fatty foods. And it's not just sugar. Refined (or "enriched") flour will give you a fast pass on the sugar roller coaster as well.

TODAY: Focus on the sugar in your breakfast meal, and cut it down or out completely. Lean on protein, fiber, and healthy fat. If you love oatmeal, try overnight oats. Smoothie lover? Try a "Green Leafy Goodness" smoothie with dark leafy greens, fresh or frozen fruit and a liquid base. Other options: avocado toast with a hard-boiled egg; organic yogurt or non-dairy yogurt with berries and sprouted grain toast; sweet potato and veggie hash with walnuts and turmeric. Pick 2–3 staple meal options. Automate and rotate.

REFLECTIONS:

WEEK #8 – DAY #39

AFFIRMATION: ***I am Valuable!***

FOUNDATION/MEDITATION: "But the very hairs of your head are all numbered. Do not fear therefore; you are of more **value** than many sparrows." *—Luke 12:7 (NKJ)*

INSPIRATION: "Your value doesn't decrease based on someone else's inability to see your worth." *—Anonymous*

MOTIVATION: I also love this quote from Max Lucado, "*You are valuable because you exist. Not because of what you do or what you have done, but simply because you are.*" Owning your value requires self-awareness. Here's a little exercise. Call or email at least 3 friends or family members and ask them for 3 words to describe you. Just tell them it's an assignment. Feel free to do more, especially if you use email. You can blind copy to target a longer list. When you get the words back, look for overlap. Find the 3 words that are most consistent and write them on a sticky note. Stick it somewhere that you will see it every day. Sometimes you just need a little reminder of just how amazing and valuable you are.

> **PRAYER STARTER:** *Thank you for knowing every hair on my head. Help me to see and own my value and my worth today and always. In Jesus' Name, Amen.*

ACTION: Sugar-Free(dom) Challenge – Day #4

Sugar is lurking and often hiding in processed and packaged foods in a big way. As a heads up, tomorrow will be your **sugar-free day**, but today, let's talk about the addictive nature of sugar. Sugar releases dopamine —your "feel-good hormone." But the "feel good" is only temporary. The euphoria from the initial blood sugar spike often ends in a crash a few hours later, which leads to craving more sugary foods. But it's also possible to retrain your brain to seek out healthier options for the same dopamine boosts. The retraining process begins by reducing and removing added sugar and finding healthier swaps like whole fruits and sweet veggies. The more you eat these healthier options, the more you will actually crave them.

TODAY: Continue with sugar-free liquids and breakfast choices. Today, the focus is on snacks. Whole fruit, organic popcorn, nuts and seeds, unsweetened Greek or coconut milk yogurt with fruit, a small smoothie (veggie and fruit), hummus on a rice cake, sweet potato, or avocado are all good choices that will help keep you energized all day long. Just aim to clear those 3+ hours in between meals, and snack only if you're hungry.

REFLECTIONS:

WEEK #8 – DAY #40

AFFIRMATION: ***I am Victorious!***

FOUNDATION/MEDITATION: "But thanks be to God! He gives us the **victory** through our Lord Jesus Christ." *—1 Corinthians 15:57 (NIV)*

INSPIRATION: "You were never created to live depressed, defeated, guilty, condemned, ashamed, or unworthy. You were created to be Victorious." *—Joel Osteen*

MOTIVATION: The order of the mantras in this devotional is alphabetical, but it's fitting that the last one is, "**you are victorious!**" I love how God works things out. You did it! It was already done before you began this adventure, but now you can do your victory dance. But don't dance too long, because the end of this book is the commencement of your "divinely designed healthy lifestyle practice." How will you be intentional from this day forward? What mantras do you need to review on a daily basis? What weekly challenges were successful for you, and how can you keep them up to maintain consistency? And most importantly, how will you celebrate crossing the finish line?

PRAYER STARTER: *Thank you for the victory. Help me to hide these mantras in my heart as a reminder of who I am, my purpose and my possibility. Thank you for helping me be committed and consistent with my whole-body health from this day forward. In Jesus' Name, Amen.*

ACTION: Sugar-Free(dom) Challenge – Day #5

Various research states that 70 percent or more of packaged foods contain added sugar. Yikes! Additionally, packaged goods often contain refined flours which, as mentioned, have a very similar impact on your blood sugar and cravings cycle. Reducing and removing processed foods from your diet can have a significant impact on your overall health. The rule is simple: "*Change your food. Change your life*!"

TODAY: Now you know why you need to significantly reduce sugar in your life. Today, you're going to do it. It's your sugar-free day! Zero added sugar. When you need a sweet taste, focus on fruit and combining single ingredient whole foods. Power up the sweet veggies you love like sweet potatoes, squash, carrots, beets and onions. Or how about a fruit and veggie smoothie? Remember, the more you eat whole clean foods, the less your body will actually crave sugar-filled low-fiber faux foods that are expanding your waistline and slowing down your life. Your body will thank you for it.

REFLECTIONS:

WHAT'S NEXT?

CONGRATULATIONS! You did it! You now know who you are in God and how fierce and powerful you are. You know you have a seed of purpose that needs a healthy temple to flourish, grow, and bless the socks off of others.

You're drinking more water, reading labels, getting more daily steps, eating only when you're hungry, loading up on more colorful veggies, getting in at least 10 minutes of cardio daily, chewing more, and reducing sugar. What?! You are #winning big time!

But here's the most important thing—don't stop! **Seek God's better daily!**

Yes, I said God's better. God's best is really beyond your comprehension. It's "*exceedingly abundantly above all we can ever ask or think*" (Ephesians 3:20 NKJV). The quest for God's best is similar to an endless pursuit of perfection, which can lead to procrastination and feeling stuck in your stuff. You are more than a conqueror, an overcomer, victorious and triumphant. You don't have time for an endless mind and body draining pursuit of "perfect health." Your life and the circumstances in your life are never going to be perfect. Just do better each day.

God's better is attainable and quantifiable. God's better in your whole-body health looks like what I call the "6 Mores"—**more purpose,**

plants, physical activity, sleep, self-care and social support than you had yesterday. But not all at the same time. Focus on one at a time! God's better looks like mindfulness and slowly but surely "Cutting the **C.R.A.P.**" (**C**-arbonated and Sugary Beverages, **R**-efined Flours & Oils, **A**-dded Sugar and Artificial Foods, and **P**-rocessed Foods) one day at a time to make room for healthier options. The beauty is that when you seek God's better every day with intentional action steps, you are actually on the road to receiving and achieving God's best in your whole-body health.

You've launched—so keep soaring. There is no perfect time to start prioritizing your health. Don't wait for a doctor, a death of a loved one, or a health event to force a change. Show up for yourself daily in purpose, on purpose today. Meditate on the Word. Fuel your body with whole clean foods and move your body consistently. As Dr. Dean Ornish says, "*Eat well. Move more. Stress less. Love more.*"

What can you do to seek God's better today?

1. **Rinse and Repeat**. If you didn't get it all in these last 8 weeks—do it again. **Commitment + Consistency = Change.** The size of your change is directly proportional to the level of your commitment and consistency. Continue to meditate on the

mantras and scripture to remind yourself that you have everything you need to do and be all that God has purposed.

2. **Be intentional**. Set a goal for yourself for the next 30 days. What area of your whole-body health needs the most focus—**faith, food or fitness**? Is it your Big Bold Why, self-esteem and belief system? Is it your sugar cravings run amok or a sedentary lifestyle? What keeps you up at night? Choose one and set a goal around it. Make it S.M.A.R.T. —**S**pecific, **M**easureable, **Ac**tionable, **R**ealistic and **T**ime-bound. Then break it down into daily and weekly action steps. You did it for 8 weeks already—keep going!

3. **Stay active in the Fit thru Faith Village**. Attaining and sustaining your "service size body" is doable, but it does take work. There are thoughts and behaviors that have been your friends for decades that aren't going to want to budge too quickly. Don't do it alone. Sustainable good health thrives in a community. Be accountable to

someone and vice versa. Make your health a hobby!

I would love to hear about your triumphs and challenges, and how I can serve you bigger, bolder and better. Please comment or contact me through the www.fitthrufaith.com website, or pop on social media to share your testimony.

Remember...Faith, Food and Fitness Fuel Your Future! Make a healthier choice today for a better tomorrow, and enjoy your spirit-powered whole-body health adventure!

Blessings & XO!

Charlie

Charlie Jordan Brookins
Your Girlfriend in Whole-Body Health
Founder, Fit thru Faith

FB: Fit thru Faith; Fit thru Faith Village
IG: @iamfitthrufaith

APPENDIX

I AM MANTRAS

A Doer	James 1:22
A Partaker of His Promise	Ephesians 3:6
A Temple	1 Corinthians 6:19
A Treasured Possession	Deuteronomy 7:6
Accepted	Romans 15:7
An Overcomer	I John 4:4
Blameless	Philippians 2:15
Blessed	Genesis 12:2
Bold	Proverbs 28:1
Chosen	John 15:16
Comforted	Psalms 23
Complete	Colossians 2:9-10
Confident	Proverbs 3:26
Courageous	Joshua 1:9
Created to Do Good Works	Ephesians 2:10
Fearless	Psalms 23:4
Fearfully and Wonderfully Made	John 15:16
Forgiven	1 John 1:9
Free	John 8:36

Free from Condemnation	Romans 8:1
Healed	Jeremiah 33:6
His Child	Galatians 3:26
His Handiwork	Ephesians 2:10
Holy	1 Peter 1: 15-16
Light	Matthew 5:14-16
Loved	Jeremiah 31 3
Made in His Image	Genesis 1:27
More than a Conqueror	Romans 8:37
New	2 Corinthians 5:17
Peaceful	Isaiah 26:3
Powerful	Acts 1:8
Qualified	Colossians 2:10
Redeemed	Ephesians 1:7
Royalty	1 Peter 2:9
Secure	Job 11:18
Strong	Ephesians 6:10
The Apple of His Eye	Psalms 17:8
Triumphant	2 Corinthians 2:14
Valuable	Luke 12:7
Victorious	I Corinthians 15:57

You are Fit thru Faith!

ABOUT THE AUTHOR

Charlie Jordan Brookins is a native of Chicago, Illinois, and a former television and film executive. She holds a bachelor of science in radio/TV/film from Northwestern University, a master of business administration from the Anderson Graduate School of Management at UCLA, and is a graduate of the Institute of Integrative Nutrition.

Now, as a certified health coach and fitness trainer, Charlie shares her passion for faith, food and fitness to help women live healthier and happier lives. In 2008, Charlie founded Fit thru Faith, an organization dedicated to empowering women to ignite their purpose, release excess weight and enjoy good health. Charlie shares her powerful message of greater service through greater health on stages nationwide, including: Bishop T.

D. Jakes' Megafest, Faithful Central Bible Church, the Musical Soul Food Festival and numerous health fairs and symposiums. Charlie currently resides in Los Angeles, California, with her husband and two sons.

CPSIA information can be obtained
at www.ICGtesting.com
Printed in the USA
LVHW081710070519
616949LV00023B/284/P